D1587977

14-120-1494

MEASUREMENTS FOR STRESSES
IN MACHINE COMPONENTS

MEASUREMENTS FOR STRESSES IN MACHINE COMPONENTS

V. F. YAKOVLEV AND I. S. INYUTIN

Translated from the Russian by

J. J. CORNISH

Translation edited by

M. L. MEYER

Senior Lecturer
Postgraduate Department of Applied Mechanics
Sheffield University

A Pergamon Press Book

THE MACMILLAN COMPANY
NEW YORK
1964

THE MACMILLAN COMPANY

60 Fifth Avenue

New York 11, N. Y.

This book is distributed by

THE MACMILLAN COMPANY

pursuant to a special arrangement with

PERGAMON PRESS LIMITED

Oxford, England

Library of Congress Catalog Card Number 63-20583

This book is a translation of the original Russian
Измерения напряжений деталей машин
(Izmereniya napryazhenii detalei mashin), published
in 1961 by Mashgiz, Moscow

CONTENTS

PREFACE

In practice, the experimental work carried out in works, laboratories, design offices and scientific research institutes requires measurement of the most diverse quantities, such as accelerations, velocities, displacements, forces, deformations, stresses and so forth.

In the design and experimental examination for the strength of machines and structures, the state of stress and strain of components and members has to be investigated frequently.

A basic and complex problem here is the study of the stresses at points inside a component, since the magnitude of these stresses may be particularly decisive in many cases, determining the service life of structures, for example contact stresses in runners, bearings, railway lines, etc.

Strength may be checked both theoretically and experimentally. Due to the complexity of individual phenomena and the consequent approximate character of the calculation schemes, theoretical calculations do not always give satisfactory results. Many problems have no theoretical solutions at all.

In recent years, therefore, experimental methods of studying the state of stress have been applied widely, alongside the development of the theory of strength calculations.

A number of measuring methods are used in the experimenta work: strain gauges, X-rays, brittle coatings, grids and photo-elasticity.

INTRODUCTION

THE DESIGN and operation of machines frequently requires an investigation of their state of stress. Similar work is carried out when new designs are made for machines and mechanisms, when their operating conditions are changed, when their strength in service is checked, and so on. The state of stress can be studied theoretically and experimentally.

Attempts to calculate theoretically the strength of structures were made as long ago as the fourteenth and sixteenth centuries by Leonardo da Vinci and Galileo [1, 2]. In the seventeenth and eighteenth centuries, the fundamentals of the theory were established by the work of Hooke, Mariotte, Bernoulli, Euler, Lomonosov, Young and others. Their work prepared the necessary basis of the classical theory for calculating the strength of members, machines and structures, which was finally formulated in the work of Cauchy, Poisson, Zhukovskii, Yasinskii, Kirpichev, Lamé, Clapeyron, Saint-Venant and others.

The development of modern experimental methods for measuring stresses started considerably later. Wire strain gauges were first used in 1938 [3], brittle coatings in 1932 [3]. Photoelasticity and X-ray diffraction have been in use since the beginning of the twentieth century [4]. Thus, the principal methods of experimental research have been developed mainly in the last 30 to 40 years.

In the initial period of mechanical engineering the dimensions of individual machine components were determined from geometrical conditions. Subsequently, the formulae of strength of materials for plane sections were applied. These calculations, however, did not indicate the real character of the stress distribution in components of complex configuration or with complex

ix

application of loads. They did not allow the determination of stress concentrations and contact or other local stresses.

The surfaces of most components of machines and mechanisms have complex shapes. The transition from one part of a component to another generally involves various forms of fillets or notches (shallow or deep, external or internal, single or multiple, circular or angular).

Practical experience in the operation of machines and mechanisms indicates that in the majority of cases their components or members fail where the shape of the body surface shows a sharp change. For example, when the average stresses in a concentration zone are 3000–3500 kg/cm^2 (42,500–50,000 lb/in^2), the maximum stresses may amount to 9000–10,000 kg/cm^2 (128,000–142,000 lb/in^2), and the strength naturally is determined by the maximum stress.

Therefore, in order to determine the actual conditions for sufficient strength, the service life of members stressed in fatigue and the optimum shape of components from the point of view of stress distribution, the stresses in regions of stress concentration must be investigated theoretically and experimentally.

The study of stress concentrations has become particularly necessary because of the increase in the operating speed of machines and the consequent increase in the dynamic action on their components

It is frequently impossible to calculate stresses theoretically. Theoretical calculations are sometimes too inaccurate because a number of premises and assumptions have to be made. In a number of cases insuperable mathematical difficulties are encountered in theoretical calculations. Problems of stress determination which have no theoretical solution are encountered in many important problems in the field of mechanical and aeronautical engineering, fluid mechanics and so on.

In these cases experimental methods of investigation play the most important role and lead to very simple or complex empirical factors. Hence, alongside theoretical investigations into the state of stress in machine components and structural members, experimental methods are acquiring greater and greater importance.

In practice, the most expedient way of studying strength problems is to use both experiment and theory and to supplement theoretical calculation by separate experimental data and coefficients. In recent years, therefore, together with a considerable improvement in calculation theory, experimental methods of investigation have been greatly developed and are becoming more and more important. Experimenters have adequately improved the measuring equipment at their disposal, thus permitting the study of diverse processes under various conditions.

In practice, the operation of machines and mechanisms has shown that in most cases wear and failure of components and members take place not only at sharp changes in the shape of the surface but also where components come in contact with one another. Components of machines and mechanisms sometimes fail as a result of contact stresses and local stresses, despite a considerable margin of safety with regard to the principal stresses of loading.

Contact stresses are mostly less dangerous at the contact surface than at a certain depth below the surface where the greatest contact shearing stresses occur, causing pitting of the material. Such a deep-pitting phenomenon is observed in escalator runners on underground railways [5, 6], in railway lines, etc.

The problem of determining stresses in the contact zone of elastic bodies, i. e. below the surface, arises whenever pressure is transmitted from one component or member to another. As has been stated, the theoretical solution of three-dimensional problems, and particularly of contact problems, presents considerable difficulties and is not possible in every practical case.

The stresses inside a component can be both residual and active. Residual stresses are those balanced inside the given body without the application of external forces. In addition to residual stresses, there may be preliminary or initial stresses in a component; such stresses arise when the component is mounted into the structure, for example stresses in tightened bolts, in prestressed reinforcements, etc.

The present book deals with a method of determining active stresses occurring inside a component when it is subjected to

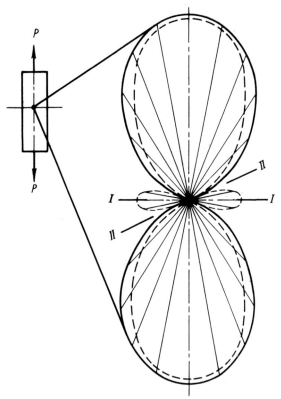

Fig. 1. Stresses and strain at a point of a linearly stressed specimen:
——— stresses: - - - - strains

dynamic loads during operation or when it is loaded by external forces.

When the external forces are removed this form of stress disappears, as do the deformations if the material is working within its elastic limit.

Most components and members are stressed three-dimension-
ally, but with the existing methods of measurement only stresses at the surface can be determined, and these do not give an
overall picture of the stress distribution. The following considerations show that the type of investigation to be adopted is substantially dependent upon the character of the state of stress.

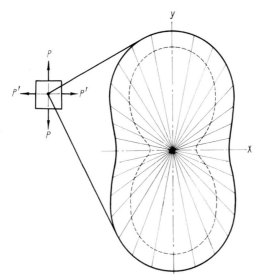

FIG. 2. Stresses and strains at a point
of a specimen in plane stress:
———————— stresses; - - - - strains

The simple relationship between strains and stresses defined
by Hooke's law

$$\sigma = \varepsilon \cdot E$$

is valid only for a linear state of stress in one direction, i.e. the
direction of the major principal strain. Figure 1 shows the picture
of the stresses and strains at a point in a linearly stressed specimen, and it is evident that in the direction I–I perpendicular
to the line of action of the forces there are no stresses but that
there are strains, while in the direction II–II there are stresses

but no strains. Thus, even for a uni-directional state of stress, the strain measured in an arbitrary direction fails to reflect the loading stresses.

In the case of a plane state of stress, illustrated diagrammatically in Fig. 2, the simple relationship between strain and stress cannot be used in any direction at all. It is well known from the theory of elasticity that Hooke's law here takes the form

$$\varepsilon_x = \frac{1}{E}(\sigma_x - \mu\sigma_y),$$

$$\varepsilon_y = \frac{1}{E}(\sigma_y - \mu\sigma_x),$$

i.e. each of the strains is determined by two stresses and, correspondingly, each of the stresses is determined by two strains.

The relationship between strains and stresses is even more complex for the three-dimensional state of stress. Analytically, the strains can be defined in terms of the stresses

$$\varepsilon_x = \frac{1}{E}[\sigma_x - \mu(\sigma_y + \sigma_x)],$$

$$\varepsilon_y = \frac{1}{E}[\sigma_y - \mu(\sigma_x + \sigma_z)],$$

$$\varepsilon_z = \frac{1}{E}[\sigma_z - \mu(\sigma_x + \sigma_y)].$$

Correspondingly, the stresses are expressed in terms of the strains by

$$\sigma_x = 2G\left[\varepsilon_x + \frac{\mu}{1-2\mu}\theta\right],$$

$$\sigma_y = 2G\left[\varepsilon_y + \frac{\mu}{1-2\mu}\theta\right],$$

$$\sigma_z = 2G\left[\varepsilon_z + \frac{\mu}{1-2\mu}\theta\right],$$

where

$$G = \frac{E}{2\,(1+\mu)}, \qquad \theta = \varepsilon_x + \varepsilon_y + \varepsilon_z.$$

It is seen from these expressions that the magnitudes of the principal stresses can only be obtained by determining the values of the three principal strains and that for a complete picture of the stress field at points inside a body in a three-dimensional state of stress, for example in a region of contact stresses, six strain components must be determined. Hence it is impossible to study the stresses inside a component by determining the strains at its surface.

CHAPTER I

BASIC METHODS OF EXPERIMENTAL STRESS ANALYSIS

SEVERAL methods of measuring strains are employed at the present time. The methods in most common use are: strain gauges, photoelasticity, X-ray diffraction, brittle coatings and dividing grids. The physical basis of these methods and the way in which they are employed are briefly described below.

1. THE PHOTOELASTIC METHOD

The photoelastic method of stress analysis [4, 10, 12, 14] is based on the fact that the majority of transparent isotropic materials become optically anisotropic under the effect of a load producing a stress. Optical anisotropy results in double refraction when light is passed through the model. Double refraction is seen in the ability of certain crystals to split a ray of light into two rays when refracting it.

Monochromatic light emanating from the source in the form of natural disordered waves is polarized and ordered, for example, into a parallel beam with a given wavelength λ and then used to illuminate the model. In plane-polarized light the waves move in parallel planes (elliptical and circular polarization also exist). The optical bench uses a polarizer to obtain polarized light.

As a result of the optical anisotropy, the vibrations of the two rays obtained after double refraction in the loaded model travel through the model plate with unequal velocities.

The linear path difference (R_t) of these two rays is directly proportional to the magnitude of the stresses; it also depends on the optical properties of the material and the thickness of the model plate. The law of photoelasticity is expressed by the equation:

$$R_t = C \cdot t \, (\sigma_1 - \sigma_2),$$

where C is the optical constant of the material, t is the thickness of the plate and σ_1, σ_2 are the principal stresses.

The vibrations of the two rays emerging from the model are recombined in one plane with the aid of another polarizing ele-

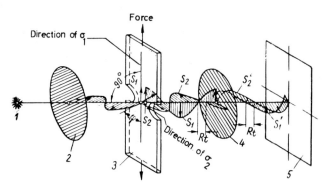

FIG. 3. Diagram of path of light in a polariscope
for stress analysis

ment called the analyser, and in this plane interference occurs. The combined vibration is projected onto a screen or a film in a camera.

A general diagram of the path of light through the instruments of a polariscope is given in Fig. 3. The natural ray obtained from the light source 1, on passing through the polarizer 2, is converted into plane-polarized light with vibrations confined to one plane.

During passage through the plate 3 under investigation, which is made from an optically active material, the ray undergoes double refraction, i.e. it is polarized in two mutually perpendicular directions and forms two rays S_1 and S_2.

If the principal stresses in the given directions of polarization of the rays are not equal then, after passing through the plate, the rays S_1 and S_2 will have a certain path difference R_t.

The vibrations of the emerging rays S_1 and S_2 are again combined in one plane with the aid of the analyser 4; interference occurs and a fringe pattern is obtained on the screen 5.

The brightness of the model image on the screen depends upon the magnitude of R_t; the greatest brightness will be found at places where $R_t = \lambda/2$, and the least brightness where $R_t = 0$ or $R_t = \lambda$.

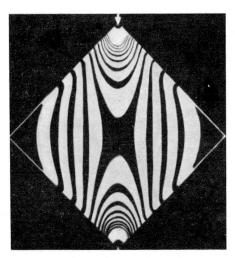

FIG. 4. Fringe pattern of a diagonally
compressed square plate

As a result, a so-called fringe pattern is obtained on the screen; this pattern is an image of alternating dark and light fringes of different orders (or fringes of different colour). Figure 4 shows the fringe pattern in a rectangular plate compressed by two forces.

Since $R_t = 2 \cdot Ct\, \tau_{max}$, a fringe is a locus for points where the principal stress difference has a given magnitude. The fringe pattern thus records all the points with given principal stress differences. After determining the value of one fringe for a given thickness and material of the model by preliminary calibration, the fringe pattern can be used to measure the magnitude of the principal stress difference at any point in the model.

The data obtained from studying plane models by the photo-elastic method can be used to construct isoclinic lines, which join points with identical slopes of the principal stresses, and isostatic lines, which are the trajectories of the principal stresses. Isoclinic and isostatic patterns are the main starting material for analysing the stresses in a model and permit to determine the magnitudes of the principal stresses by special techniques.

The optical method can be used to resolve not only plane problems but also three-dimensional problems. When solving three-dimensional problems, the model is loaded at a temperature of 100–120° C and in this state is gradually cooled; the stresses are said to be "frozen in." The "frozen" model is then cut into plane slices which are studied in plane-polarized light.

Photoelasticity is used to solve problems under conditions of plane and three-dimensional strain with various systems of loading. Its use has a number of advantages: it gives a visual picture of the stressed state (fringe patterns in the plane problem); the influence of various shapes of the component can be studied; various systems of loading can be applied, etc. The main disadvantages are its laboriousness; the complexity of the manufacture of models of the component to be studied, particularly for three-dimensional problems; and also the necessity of using materials with particular properties (such as optical activity, minimum edge effect, good transparency, isotropy, etc.).

The latest research in the field of photoelasticity, namely the use of new materials such as epoxy resins, Mikhmimash, and Viskhomlit (phenoplast), together with the use of new optical apparatus, has considerably improved the method, but it has not succeeded in solving the main problem, which is to make the process of studying and solving three-dimensional problems with dynamic loads less complicated and less laborious.

To obtain the final results it is necessary to carry out a laborious intermediate process of plotting graphs accompanied, as a rule, by interpolation of the experimentally obtained graphs. All this affects the final results of the analysis.

The error in measurements made by the photoelastic method varies, $\pm$ 1 to $\pm 5\%$ for plane models, and ± 5 to $\pm$ 20% for three-dimensional models.

2. THE X-RAY DIFFRACTION METHOD

The X-ray method [15, 16, 17, 18, 19, 20, 21] is based on a comparison of X-ray diffraction photographs of deformed and undeformed metals. Deformations of metals cause distortions of their crystal lattices which alter the diffraction pattern of an X-ray photograph. The X-ray diffraction method is the only method sufficiently sensitive to measure internal residual stresses. It can be used to measure stresses over small lengths (of the order of $1-3$ mm), and to provide an experimental solution for such problems as the determination of residual stresses in welded joints, the magnitude and character of the strains and stresses in work-hardened zones, of stress concentrations, etc.

In investigations of the stressed state it is usual to distinguish four forms of elastic stresses:

1. Elastic stresses that are balanced by the external forces (active stresses); these disappear completely when the effect of the external (active) forces ceases.

2. First-order residual stresses that are balanced within the given specimen or within individual regions of it. When the effect of the force ceases these stresses do not disappear. First-order stresses are due to plastic and elastic deformations under an inhomogeneous state of stress caused by the character of the applied forces, the shape of the specimen, heat treatment and so forth.

3. Second-order residual stresses that are balanced within the limits of one or a few crystals. These stresses occur as a result of plastic deformations and also as a result of microscopic inclusions of foreign particles in the basic material.

4. Third-order residual stresses that are balanced within the limits of a few lattice units. They occur in solid solutions such as martensite.

All these stresses often exist simultaneously, thus complicating the use of the X-ray diffraction method.

The X-ray diffraction method of determining residual stresses is based on changes in the diffraction pattern due to deformations in the crystal lattice of the metals, in particular asterism (distortion of spots), line broadening, reduction in line intensity and line displacement.

Asterism occurs when X-rays are reflected from curved crystal lattices. It is seen in elongated (instead of circular) diffraction

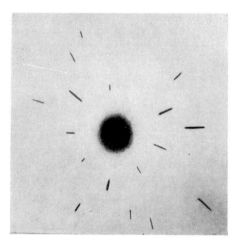

FIG. 5. X-ray diffraction photograph
of a strained metal

spots (Fig. 5). The stressed state can be evaluated by the degree of elongation (the length of the "tails").

Line broadening occurs during plastic deformation of a metal and is the result of differences in the lattice parameter in the region covered by the rays. It begins to appear in the initial stages of deformation and grows with the amount of deformation.

Figure 6 shows a representation of X-ray photographs of a deformed (a) and an undeformed (b) specimen.

Reduction in line intensity is brought about by the displacement of individual atoms from their position of equilibrium (third-order stresses). This phenomenon is also evidence of plastic deformation of a metal.

Line displacement is caused by first-order stresses under which the regions covered by the rays are subjected to approximately uniform deformation. In this case, the change in the interatomic distances causes a proportional line displacement. The measurement of first-order elastic stresses is based on the relation between the interatomic distances of the crystal lattice and the magnitude of the stresses. Comparison of the distances measured on a stressed specimen with data obtained from an unstressed specimen either experimentally or theoretically permits determination of the magnitude of the stresses. If this work

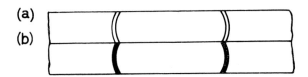

FIG. 6. X-ray diffraction effect — line broadening

is carried out well, it is possible to achieve highly accurate measurements. In steels, for example, the error does not exceed ± 2 kg/cm² (30 lb/in²) [15].

It should be noted that the apparatus and experimental set-up are comparatively complex so that X-ray diffraction is used but rarely for the determination of first-order stresses. It is more usual to employ mechanical methods, for example sectioning of the component [20, 21].

Second-order residual stresses occur as a result of plastic deformations of the metal. They appear on the X-ray photograph in the form of line broadening caused by the reflection of the rays from the atomic planes in the deformation zones. The residual stresses deform these planes to different degrees and also change the lattice spacing in individual regions to different degrees. To determine the second-order stresses it is necessary to compare by photometry two X-ray photographs obtained under identical conditions for a deformed and an undeformed specimen, and then to evaluate them for the magnitude of the residual stresses.

In spite of the fact that X-ray diffraction is the only method of measuring residual stresses without destroying the surface of the component it is used rarely on account of its low accuracy, its complexity and the amount of labour it requires (particularly when first- and second-order stresses are present simultaneously).

Among the disadvantages of the method which reduce its accuracy are: changes of the crystal lattice parameter in the standard; the influences exerted by temperature variations within the crystal lattice, by the state (fineness of the finish) of the surface of the specimen, and by the inhomogeneity of the solid solution in the metal.

In addition, it should be noted that when X-ray photographs are taken the components are X-rayed for several hours at each point, the stress is studied at a small depth from the surface of the specimens (hundredths of a millimetre), and in practice it is the plane problem that is being solved, whereas the real problem is the three-dimensional state of stress.

3. THE BRITTLE COATINGS METHOD

The substance of the brittle coatings method is that a thin film of a special brittle lacquer is applied to the surface of the component to be studied [22, 23, 24, 10, 3].

The properties of the lacquer are such that cracks appear when the strains increase in the lacquer at a given point up to a certain limiting magnitude depending upon the properties of the lacquer coating and the experimental conditions. The sequence in which these cracks appear corresponds to the state of stress in the testpiece. The cracks appear first at the most highly stressed points (Fig. 7).

The cracks are perpendicular to the direction of the isostatics, i.e. of curved lines the tangents to which indicate the direction of the principal stresses at any given point.

Since the surface of any three-dimensional body under investigation will be in a linear or plane state of stress, the direction of the second principal stress (perpendicular to the first) is everywhere tangential to the cracks.

The overall picture of the crack distribution permits a general evaluation for the strength and rigidity of the component under investigation (Fig. 8). The location and direction of the first cracks in the lacquer coating corresponds as a rule to the location and direction of cracks that would appear as a result of fatigue phenomena during service of the component.

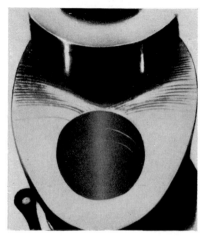

FIG. 7. Pattern of cracks in a brittle coating on a crankshaft (intensified by etching)

To give satisfactory results the brittle lacquer must satisfy a number of requirements: it must fully repeat the strains of the surfaces being studied, have a high Young's modulus and low elongation, and have stable mechanical properties (in all parts and in all periods of strain). Various research workers recommend a number of different lacquer compositions [22, 10] for the application of brittle coatings. The best of these are solutions of products from the treatment of wood resins and hydrogen sulphide, with additions of various plasticizers. Ceramic lacquers are also very good [3]. The accuracy of the measurements depends largely on the quality of the application of the lacquer to the surface of the workpiece, so that the surface must be specially treated and the lacquer applied under particular temperature conditions in a layer of uniform thickness with no spots or bare patches.

The sensitivity of the method reaches 3×10^{-4} to 25×10^{-4} strain or 600 to 5000 kg/cm² (8500–70,000 lb/in.²) for steel.

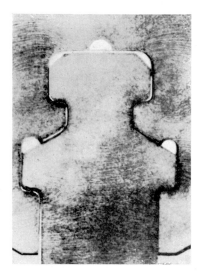

Fig. 8. Pattern of cracks in a flat component

The accuracy of the measurements also depends greatly upon the conditions under which the experiments are carried out (the temperature and humidity during the test, the time taken for the coating to dry, the thickness of the layer of lacquer, the way in which the load is applied, etc.).

The measuring error depends on the character of the stresses being studied: the greatest errors are found in tensile tests, the smallest in torsion tests. The accuracy also depends on the character of the loading; it is ± 10 to 15% for static tests and $\pm 25\%$ for dynamic tests [10].

One of the main difficulties in increasing the accuracy of the measurements is that the strain at which cracks begin to appear in the lacquer applied to the component under test does not correspond to the strain at which the lacquer applied to the calibration strip begins to crack. In addition, the determination of only one principal strain (by the size of the cracks) in a plane state of stress does not allow an accurate assessment of the corresponding principal stress, and the other principal stress has to be neglected completely.

The brittle coatings method is normally used only for a qualitative analysis of the stressed state at the surface of a component. The advantages of the method are that an accurate picture is obtained of the principal stresses and strains over an entire surface; it reveals regions of stress concentration and places where cracks are likely to appear under service conditions; it is simple and can be readily understood.

This method can best be employed in combination with strain gauge measurements. After the stress concentrations in the component and the direction of the principal strains have been found by the use of brittle coatings, the stresses can be measured with the aid of strain gauges.

4. THE GRID METHOD

The grid method [10, 25] consists in applying grids of given shape and dimensions (rectangular, circular, etc.) to the surface of a specimen. When the specimen is loaded its fibres are deformed and the grid units change their shape and dimensions.

The grid method of studying a component gives the following results:

(a) the change in shape (for example with circular grids) leads to the direction of the principal stresses;

(b) the change in distance between grid lines leads to the linear strain of the component;

(c) the overall picture of the change in the shape and dimensions of the grid units indicates the most highly stressed regions and the places where plastic deformations have appeared;

(d) calculations with the experimental data give the maximum shear.

The distance between the lines forming the individual units is 0.25–2 mm and over. With such a comparatively small base length it is possible to study regions with a large stress gradient, for example stress concentrations. The method allows investigation of stresses with large strains as also under conditions of dynamic loading and at high temperatures.

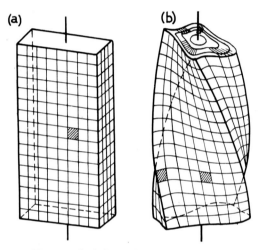

FIG. 9. A deformed specimen with a
grid marked on it

Figure 9 gives the simplest example for the use of the grid method in studying the character of the plastic deformations in torsion tests [25]. The surface of the testpiece is first divided into rectangular grids of given dimensions [Fig. 9 (a)]. After the torsion test the shape of the units has changed [Fig. 9 (b)]. From the change in the outline of the units and the magnitude of their dimensional changes, the picture of the plastic deformation of the surface of the specimen can be studied.

The main disadvantage of the grid method is its comparatively low accuracy for strain measurements (up to ±6%), particularly with a small base length and strains less than 5% [10].

The grid method is used mainly for the study of deformations in members and models made out of materials having a low modulus of elasticity (such as rubber), and for the study of plastic deformations in other materials (in processes involving forming of metals by pressure, etc.).

5. EXTENSOMETRY

The most frequently employed method of measuring stresses is by the use of extensometers or strain gauges [9, 10, 3, 11, 12, 13, 26]. Stress measurements may be made with many types of strain gauges such as mechanical, optical, vibrating-wire or electro-acoustic, pneumatic and various electrical devices.

Mechanical strain gauges

These strain gauges use various systems of magnifying the deformations under consideration. They give a reading magnification of 500—1000 times of the deformation being measured. The shorter the base length of a strain gauge, the greater must be the degree of magnification. This type of strain gauge is used mainly for measuring strains under static loads.

The most widely used type is the Huggenberger extensometer. A dial indicator is sometimes also incorporated in mechanical strain gauges.

Optical strain gauges

The required degree of magnification is here achieved by using as a pointer a ray of light reflected from a mirror. The angle of tilt of the mirror depends upon the magnitude of the displacement to be measured.

Vibrating-wire (electro-acoustic) strain gauges

Developed by Davidenkov, these strain gauges are based on the change in frequency of the natural oscillations of a wire the tension of which varies with the displacement in the surface of the workpiece. The oscillations of the wire are converted into electrical oscillations and the frequency of these is measured by one means or another.

Pneumatic strain gauges

These strain gauges are based on the variations in the rate of flow of air passing through a nozzle with a degree of opening depending upon the magnitude of the displacement.

Electrical strain gauges

These are the gauges most widely used. Electrical strain measurement makes it possible to analyse the stressed state of components subjected to static and dynamic loading, and the method permits measurement of the local principal stresses in linear and plane states of stress. The gauges may have a comparatively short base length (down to 1—1.5 mm), small dimensions and low inertia, these factors being particularly important for the measurement of dynamic phenomena.

Electrical strain gauges have various types of transducer: resistive, capacitive, photoelectric, magnetostrictive, etc. The most common, however, are the resistive transducers. Of the electrical strain gauges only those based on resistance changes can be used to measure the stresses inside components of machines and mechanisms.

6. THE PHYSICAL FUNDAMENTALS OF THE OPERATION OF ELECTRIC RESISTANCE WIRE STRAIN GAUGES, THEIR MAKE-UP AND PROPERTIES

A great deal of literature has been devoted to wire strain gauges [27, 3, 9, 10, 11, 22]; it is therefore not thought necessary in this section to give more than a brief description which will be sufficient for an understanding of the subsequent chapters.

The physical basis of the method

The use of wire strain gauges is based on the following concepts:

1. The elongations of the fibers of a material are proportional to the stresses produced in them (Hooke's law).

2. When a bar is strained, not only its length changes but also its cross-section. The elongation and the change in transverse dimensions are connected by Poisson's ratio.

3. If a wire grid is cemented to the surface of a specimen under test so that it fully follows the strain of the specimen, then its length l and its cross-sectional area S will change. In addition, experience shows that the deformation of a wire also changes its resistivity. Since

$$R = \varrho \, \frac{l}{S} \, ,$$

all the three parameters defining the electrical resistance of the wire change under the effect of the deformations transferred to the wire from the component to which it is cemented.

A linear dependence exists here between the unit strain of the wire grid ε and the relative change of resistance $\varDelta R/R$ of the gauge,

$$\frac{\varDelta R}{R} = K \cdot \varepsilon,$$

where K, the gauge factor, depends upon the material of the gauge and is usually 1.9–2.1 for constantan wire.

The grid of wire strain gauges is made from alloys possessing a comparatively high gauge factor K and a low temperature coefficient of resistance. These properties can be found in constantan and nichrome for example. The diameter of the wire varies between 12 and 35 μ $(0.5–1.5 \times 10^{-3}$ in.); it has such a fineness because of the necessity to make the gauges comparatively short and with a fairly high resistance. A small diameter is also necessary to prevent the wire grid from slipping after it has been cemented to the specimen, i.e. for a firmer fixing of the wire grid to the specimen.

The characteristics of the strain gauges depend to a great extent upon the material of the wire; the wire must therefore be carefully examined and heat treated (annealed) [27, 41]. The main characteristics of the wires most widely used for the manufacture of strain gauges are given in Table 1, reproduced from data given in [27].

TABLE 1.

Material and its composition	Gauge factor $K = \dfrac{\Delta R}{R} \Big/ \dfrac{\Delta l}{l}$	Temperature coefficient of resistance (per °C)	Resistivity in Ω mm²/m	Thermal emf with copper in steam, in μ V/°C	Ultimate strength in kg/mm²	Temperature coefficient of linear expansion
Constantan (60% Cu + + 40% Ni)..........	1.9—2.1	$(-50-+50) \times 10^{-6}$	0.46—0.5	47	65	$(14-15) \times \times 10^{-6}$
Nichrome (80% Ni + + 20% Cr)..........	2.0	$(150-170) \times 10^{-6}$	0.9—1.7	22	—	14×10^{-6}
Iron–chromium aluminium alloy No. 2 (22.3% Cr+ + 4.8% Al + 0.035% Co + Fe remainder)...	2.8—2.9	$(7-20) \times 10^{-6}$	1.35—1.55	5—6	120—130	—
Manganin (84% Cu + + 12% Mn + 4% Ni)	0.47—0.5	$(-30-+10) \times 10^{-6}$	0.4—0.45	2	—	$(16-18) \times \times 10^{-6}$
Chromel (65% Ni + 25% Fe + 10% Cr)........	2.5	$(100-500) \times 10^{-6}$	0.7—1.1	16	—	14.8×10^{-6}
Platinum iridium alloy (95% Pt + 5% Ir)....	5.8	$\pm\ 3.9 \times 10^{-6}$	0.24	—	—	13×10^{-6}

As a result of the heat treatment (annealing) at a temperature of 650—800° C, the strength and strain-measuring characteristics of the wire change substantially. Thus, according to data given by Tisenko [41], annealing of constantan wire of 0.025 mm in dia. for one hour in a vacuum at a temperature of 650° C reduces its temperature coefficient of resistance 1.33 times, its rupture stress 1.45 times, its percentage elongation 2.34 times, increases its gauge factor by 11% and reduces its ultimate strength 1.44 times.

At present, the following types of wire strain gauge are mainly used:

1. Strain gauges with a wire grid in a single plane (zig-zag wound) as shown in Fig. 10 (a). This is the form of gauge most widely used; its base length is usually from 5—25 mm.

(a)

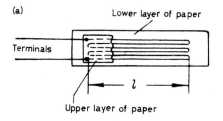

Lower layer of paper

Terminals

l

Upper layer of paper

(b)

Spiral winding

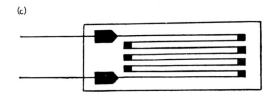

(c)

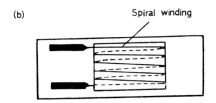

(d)

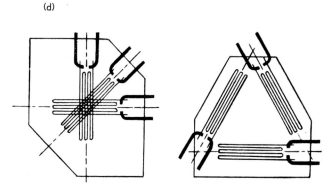

FIG. 10. Types of electric-resistance strain gauge

2

2. Strain gauges with a wire grid in two planes separated by a layer of paper and adhesive (mandril wound) as seen in Fig. 10 (b). This form of gauge is used most often with short base lengths of 5 mm and below.
3. Foil strain gauges [Fig. 10 (c)] have a number of advantages over wire strain gauges; they can be made in any shape and have a lower cross-sensitivity.
4. For complex stresses, multi-grid strain gauges are used in the form of rosettes [rectangular, delta rosettes, etc., Fig. 10 (d)].

Depending upon their design, the wire grids of strain gauges are manufactured with the aid of devices and machines of various types (manual, semi-automatic or automatic). Strain gauges with a wire grid woven into a fabric backing on a loom also exist. Foil gauges are produced by etching previously prepared foils [42].

The terminals are fixed to the grid wire by soldering or welding (electric spark or contact welding, see Section 73).

Cementing the gauge grid to the workpiece.
Cements based on epoxy resins

The result of the measurements depends largely on the care with which the wire grid is cemented to the surface of the workpiece. During measurements the strain gauge should follow faithfully the strains of the workpiece over its entire length.

Before cementing, the surface of the workpiece should be given a surface finish not lower than ▽▽ 6 (63 μ in. CLA maximum roughness) [10] and the machining marks should be perpendicular to the final direction of the grid wires; the surface should be degreased with acetone, toluene or alcohol.

Various types of cement can be used to affix the wire grids; these include celluloid, carbinol, bakelite, bakelite-phenol (BF-2, BF-4), siliconitroglyptal adhesives and others. Their compositions and the way in which they are used are described fairly extensively in the literature [10, 27, 3].

Recently new cements have appeared based on epoxy resins; some of their characteristics are given below. They are used for cementing metals, china, glass, plastics, etc., and their composition is shown in Table 2.

TABLE 2.

Name of original products	Type or Trade mark	National Standard or Technical Specification	Quantity of component in parts by weight for cements of type					
			EM—1	EM—2	EM—3	EM—4	EM—5	EM—6
Epoxy resin	ED—5	VTUMRTP M686—56	—	100	100	100	100	100
Epoxy resin	ED—6	VTU MKHP M646—55	100	—	—	—	—	—
Triphenyl phosphate		UTMKHP 637—47	—	—	—	20	20	—
Dibutyl phthalate	Commercial or reagent	GOST 3863—47 or 2102—51	25	30	30	20	20	30
Ground mica		GOST 855—41	20	25	—	—	20	—
Powdered quartz	PK—2, PK—3	TU MS and IP 1954	—	—	20	30	—	30—50
Ground talc		GOST 879—52	—	—	—	50	25	—
Hexamethylene diamine	Commercial or reagent	TUMKHP 3161—53 or VTRU 1072—54	10	13	13	13	13	13
Polyethylene polyamine		VTUMKHP B4—26—56	—	—	—	—	—	—

Note 1: When preparing cements of type EM—2, EM—3, EM—4, EM—5 and EM—6 it is permitted to use epoxy resin ED—5; the amount of curing agent then is 10 parts by weight of the composition
Note 2: When preparing cements of type EM—2 to EM—6, polyethylene polyamines can be used

Depending upon the required strength and other factors, the composition of a cement based on epoxy resins can vary within the limits shown in Table 3.

TABLE 3.

Name of components	Type of resin	
	ED—5	ED—6
Polyethylene polyamines	9—10	7— 8
Dibutyl phthalate	7—15	7—25
Powdered quartz	10—70	10—50
Ground mica	10—60	10—40

Note 1: The table shows the composition for 100 parts by weight of resin
Note 2: The filler employed is either powdered quartz or ground mica

This type of cement is prepared in the following manner: the resin, dibutyl phthalate and the filler are weighed off. The chosen components are heated in a thermostatically controlled vessel to a temperature of 80–90° C and mixed. The mixture is then allowed to cool to a temperature of 15–20° C.

The hardener (polyethylene polyamine) is weighed out separately and introduced by careful stirring into the basic mixture immediately before use.

The cement retains its properties for 20 min to one hour after final preparation. The polymerization time at room temperature is not more than 24 hr. It is useful to heat the cemented joint to a temperature of 60° C for 3–4 hr. The strength of the joint is not less than 50–70 kg/cm² (700–1000 lb/in.²). The cement possesses high dielectric properties.

After the cement has dried, the minimum resistance to earth of the strain gauges should not be less than 50–100 MΩ [3]; for static and prolonged measurements it should not be below 100 MΩ.

7. STRAIN-GAUGE CIRCUITS

A wire strain gauge can be connected up either in a potentiometer circuit [Fig. 11 (a)], or in a single bridge circuit [Fig. 11 (b)].

A potentiometer circuit is used with d.c. current when only the variable component of the measured quantity is of interest; the d.c. component of the voltage drop on the strain gauge R_n is then filtered out by a blocking capacitor C and a cathode ray tube is normally employed as the output meter (measuring device).

The single bridge circuit of Fig. 11 (b) is the one most often used for electric strain measurement. The active strain gauges are connected into one or two arms of the bridge.

A bridge circuit can be used in two ways: *(a)* as a balanced bridge—the null method—when the result of measurements is determined with the bridge in equilibrium; and *(b)* as an unbalanced bridge—the direct measuring method—when the result of measurements is determined with the bridge out of equilibrium by the indications of a meter in the diagonal of the bridge.

A balanced bridge gives very accurate measurements of the resistance change (up to 0.01% [28]), but can be used only for static measurements.

An unbalanced bridge does not provide such a high degree of accuracy and is used most frequently in the investigation of

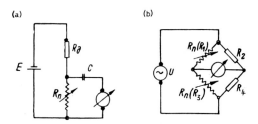

FIG. 11. Electric circuits for wire strain gauges

dynamic phenomena. This method is the fundamental measuring arrangement for the measurement of stresses by electric strain gauges. A serious disadvantage of the unbalanced bridge is the dependence of the instrument readings on the voltage of the supply source, which often leads to the necessity of using voltage stabilizers.

It is well known that a bridge is balanced when the ratio of the resistances in the arms [Fig. 11 (b)] satisfies the condition:

$$R_1 R_4 = R_2 R_3.$$

This condition must be fulfilled before measurements are taken.

When the bridge is unbalanced, i.e. when the resistance of the active gauge changes due to the strain to be measured, the current in the output diagonal of the bridge is:

$$I_u = \frac{U\,(R_1 R_4 - R_2 R_3)}{R_u\,(R_1 + R_2)\,(R_3 + R_4) + R_1\,R_2\,(R_3 + R_4) + R_3\,R_4\,(R_1 + R_2)}.$$

Depending on the character of the strains to be measured, one, two or four active strain gauges can be connected into the arms

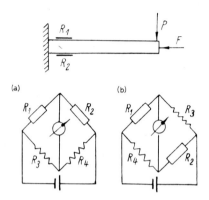

(a)   (b)

FIG. 12. Bridge circuits for two
active strain gauges

of the bridge in different ways. For example, when measuring only strains due to bending, two active strain gauges R_1 and R_2

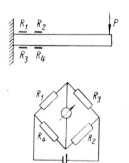

FIG. 13. Bridge circuit for four
active strain gauges

are connected as shown in Fig. 12 (a), while, when measuring only strains due to the longitudinal force, the strain gauges are connected as in Fig. 12 (b). In this way the influence exerted on the readings of the measuring device by the strains due to the direct force is excluded in the first circuit, and the influence exerted by the bending strains is excluded in the second. Other combinations of strain gauge connections may be employed. For example, when measuring bending strains it is possible to use four strain gauges connected as shown in Fig. 13.

Balancing the bridge

For all operating conditions (balanced or unbalanced) the bridge must be balanced before measurements are taken. A bridge energized by alternating current must be balanced for resistive

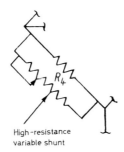

High-resistance
variable shunt

FIG. 14. Shunt for bridge
balancing

and reactive components and it is therefore necessary to provide two controllable elements in the bridge circuit. With direct current the bridge balance can be controlled by one element.

In some cases the balancing element is a slide-wire or rheostat connected in series with the constant resistance arm (R_3 or R_4); in others the constant resistance arm is best shunted by a slide-wire with a high resistance (Fig. 14).

Temperature compensation of a strain gauge

Since the resistance change of an active strain gauge under the strain to be measured is extremely small, great attention must be paid to compensate for the changes of resistance caused by fluctuations in the temperature; both these changes of resistance, that caused by the strain being measured and that caused by temperature fluctuations, may be of the same order of magnitude.

The change in resistance produced by temperature fluctuations may be due to two causes. First of all, the coefficients of linear expansion of the gauge wire and the workpiece are not as a rule identical. If the coefficient of linear expansion β of the workpiece is less than that of the gauge wire, then the wire grid cemented to the workpiece undergoes a compressive strain when the temperature rises. This phenomenon is observed, for example on steel specimens ($\beta = 11 \times 10^{-6}$ in./in. °C) with strain gauges made from constantan wire ($\beta = 14 \times 10^{-6}$ in./in. °C). The measuring error in this case will reach 6 kg/cm² (85 lb/in²) for a change in temperature of 1° C. If the linear expansion coefficients are in an inverse ratio, for example if a constantan strain gauge is cemented to aluminium ($\beta = 27 \times 10^{-6}$ in./in. °C), the wire grid undergoes a tensile strain. The error then reaches 25–30 kg/cm² (350–430 lb/in²) per °C.

Secondly, a change in temperature causes a change in the electrical resistance of the grid wire. The temperature coefficient of the electrical resistance of nichrome, for example, is 150–170 × 10⁻⁶ per °C.

When wire strain gauges are used, both these factors act simultaneously and their overall effect on steel [27] will be about 12 kg/cm² (170 lb/in²) per °C; with less favourable combinations of the characteristics of the materials, for aluminium say, the error may be as much as 30–40 kg/cm² (430–570 lb/in²) per °C.

The effect of temperature on the resistance of a strain gauge can be compensated quite well by connecting two identical strain gauges into two adjacent arms of a bridge. If both gauges cannot be made active (as in Fig. 12, for example), then a dummy gauge is connected into the arm adjacent to that of the active gauge.

The best method is to stick the compensating gauge to the same testpiece as, and next to, the active gauge. In any event it must be affixed to material of the same type as the workpiece and placed under identical temperature conditions.

In the experiments carried out by the authors, temperature compensation was provided by strain gauges cast into special components used for compensation and placed during testing under temperature conditions analogous to those of the testpiece.

8. MEASURING EQUIPMENT

The equipment used for electrical strain measurement can be divided into equipment for measuring static and dynamic strains. Certain types of strain measuring devices are universal and can be used for both static and dynamic strains.

Depending upon the frequency characteristics of the strains to be measured, the equipment for dynamic measurements can be [10]:

(a) of the universal type for the measurement of strains from 0 to 3000 c/s;

(b) suitable for the measurement of dynamic strains in the frequency range between 20 and 5000 c/s;

(c) suitable for the measurement of dynamic strains in highly dynamic phenomena up to 50,000 c/s and above.

The magnitude of the strains to be measured depends on the characteristics of the material of the testpiece and on the magnitude of the stresses; in the majority of cases it varies between 1×10^{-6} and 1×10^{-2} in./in.

The recording of such small strains in instruments for dynamic measurement generally requires the use of electronic amplifying equipment connected between the measuring bridge and the dynamic recorder because galvanometer elements with a natural oscillation frequency of several kilocycles per second and above require a current in the order of 2–20 mA, whereas the current at the output terminals of the bridge is not normally in excess of a few dozen microamperes.

Circuits without electronic amplifiers can be used for measuring static strains and low-frequency dynamic strains. In this case, with a bridge circuit for the strain gauges, highly sensitive galvanometers with scale deflections of the order of $5 \times 10^{-7}-1 \times 10^{-9}$ amp per division or low-frequency galvo elements of electromagnetic recorders can be connected to the output terminals of the bridge.

In highly dynamic processes with a frequency up to 50,000 c/s and over, electromagnetic recorders cannot be used and are replaced by cathode ray oscilloscopes with d.c. amplifiers.

Multi-point equipment for 100 or more positions is usually employed for static measurements; the most advanced circuits of this type have a self-balancing bridge. Such instruments, for example the automatic electronic strain-measuring device developed by the Leningrad Machine Works, give a forty times more rapid measurement than manually balanced gauges.

Equipment for dynamic measurements (electronic amplifiers and oscillographs) can have one or more channels. Unlike static measurement, the measurement of dynamic strains must be carried out simultaneously at all the points to be investigated on the component. Since the equipment normally has only a limited number of channels (10–12), the measurements may have to be repeated with other strain gauges switched into the circuit.

When selecting the measuring equipment for dynamic strains, not only the range of strains to be measured but also the ratio of the frequency characteristics of the equipment and of the phenomena under investigation must be considered. The carrier frequency should not be less than 10 times the frequency of the phenoma [27]. If the carrier frequency is only 3–5 times higher than the frequency to be measured, only the intensity of the phenomena can be evaluated, not their complete outline.

The amplifying equipment employed by the author in his experimental studies is described in Section 17.

CHAPTER II

THE ELECTRICAL MEASUREMENT OF STRESSES INSIDE SOLIDS WITH SPECIAL RESISTANCE STRAIN GAUGES

IN THIS chapter the basic concepts of the electric strain gauge method for measuring stresses inside machine components are given. Data on the technique of conducting the experimental work, the choice of material, the preparation of models, the preparation and installation of special transducers are included, together with a description of the devices used and the electrical strain-measuring apparatus.

The substance of the method is that special wire strain gauges with a short gauge length are placed into prepared moulds for the model of the component or structural element. The strain gauges are then potted in a very strong mass made from high-molecular compounds. After this has been allowed to cure and the model has been machined to the required dimensions, static or dynamic systems of forces are applied and the strains in the model on test are picked up by the embedded wire strain gauges.

9. THE MATERIAL FOR THE MODELS

The experimental investigations leading to a determination of the character, distribution and magnitude of the internal stresses in various machine elements have been carried out with models.

The magnitude of the loads applied to the models is chosen so that the material from which the models are made remains in the elastic range. This permits a comparison of experimental data (strains and stresses) with results of the classical theory of elasticity, here understood to be the theory of linear elasticity of a homogeneous isotropic body. It is well known that the basis of the classical theory of elasticity is the concept of an elastic, linearly deformable body. In the experiments, the most important properties of the prototype are simulated in a model of the component namely, ideal elasticity, spherical isotropy, perfect homogeneity, low deformation, and also linear dependence between strains and stresses.

Assumption of these properties in their entirety, or partially where this is sufficient, permits the solution of a wide range of problems in strength calculations. The results obtained are mostly in satisfactory agreement with practical data [1].

To investigate experimentally the stresses inside bodies by electrical strain measurement with special short gauge-length wire strain gauges, one must select a material that satisfies the listed requirements. In other words, the material chosen for the models must have a relatively high strength and elastic limit, be isotropic and homogeneous, possess a low deformability, and conform to Hooke's law during the experiments. In addition, the material must satisfy a number of other requirements connected with the experimental set-up.

To avoid machining difficulties the material should not be too brittle, but at the same time it must be hard enough for clamping during machining or other operations so that it does not suffer local plastic deformation.

The material should have a fairly high modulus of elasticity so that the strains in the models are not too great and their shape remains practically unchanged.

The material must have constant properties during moderate changes in temperature, not show any noticeable mechanical creep giving a continuous increase in strain for a constant load, and have a low melting point for ease of casting of the models. It should also be possible to machine the models on ordinary lathes or with the aid of a hand cutting tool; otherwise the cost of the models will be too high, particularly if they are of complex shape.

If the measurement of the stresses inside the model is to be carried out with the aid of special unbonded wire strain gauges, the material must also possess good dielectric and adhesive properties.

All these requirements are satisfied most fully by plastic materials.

Plastics based on high-molecular organic compounds possess several valuable properties. There exist plastics of high heat and sound insulating properties with a specific weight ten times smaller than that of cork. On an average, plastics are two to three times lighter than aluminium and five to eight times lighter than steel. In addition, there exist plastics of a strength exceeding that of many types of steel [29].

When plastics are used for machine components, mechanisms, structural members, etc., a large number of problems inevitably arises regarding their strength characteristics, the selection of a rational shape and so forth.

It has been shown that the range of characteristics of plastics is far wider than, for example, that of metals. Therefore, special techniques and conditions for testing plastics materials must be developed.

For the purpose of measuring the stresses in models, many of the materials of the optical method of stress analysis can be used. The given requirements are fulfilled, for example, by materials based on epoxy resins, by LGU Bakelite, IM–44 (a type of Viskhomlit), Mikhmimash, Merblet, Trolon, and others. The authors have used epoxy resins for their models.

As regards individual properties there are several polymers more suitable than epoxy resins, but very seldom does such a happy combination of physical, mechanical, dielectric and chemical properties occur in a single material. Hence epoxy resins are used in the most widely varying fields and in some cases have made it possible to solve formerly insoluble problems.

Epoxy resins are the condensation products of epichlorohydrin and a diatomic or polyatomic phenol, usually diphenylol propane, which was first produced by the Russian scientist A. N. Dianin in 1891, and has been called 'dian' in his honour [30].

'Dian' epoxy resins have the following structure:

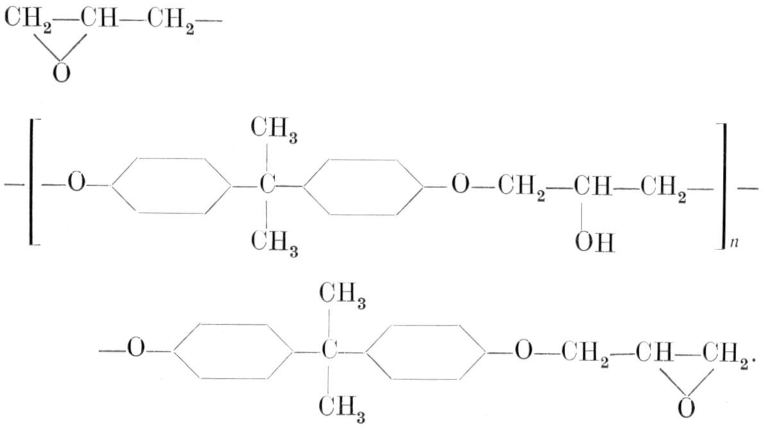

$$CH_2-CH-CH_2-$$
(with epoxide O bridge)

$$\left[-O-\left\langle\right\rangle-\overset{\overset{CH_3}{|}}{C}-\left\langle\right\rangle-O-CH_2-CH-CH_2- \right]_n$$
(with CH₃ below the C, and OH below the central CH)

$$-O-\left\langle\right\rangle-\overset{\overset{CH_3}{|}}{C}-\left\langle\right\rangle-O-CH_2-CH-CH_2.$$
(with CH₃ below the C, and epoxide O bridge at the end)

As can be seen from this structural formula, each resin molecule has at its ends epoxide groups that are connected by a chain of carbon atoms alternating with ether oxygen. Such a chain structure gives high chemical resistance and good adhesion.

When the resin solidifies by the cross-linking of its molecular chains, its molecular weight increases and a number of useful properties are formed. The cross-linkages can be made either through the epoxide or through the hydroxyl groups, or through both at once.

The relatively widely spaced position of the cross-linkages maintains the possibility of a certain amount of internal rotation of the sections of the chains located between linkages. This ensures good resistance to impact and the retention of adhesion under comparatively high stresses.

The curing agent used by the authors is the anhydride of an organic dibasic acid, actually maleic anhydride.

When anhydrides are used the hydroxide groups as well as the epoxide groups participate in the curing reaction, as is evident from the reaction diagram [30]:

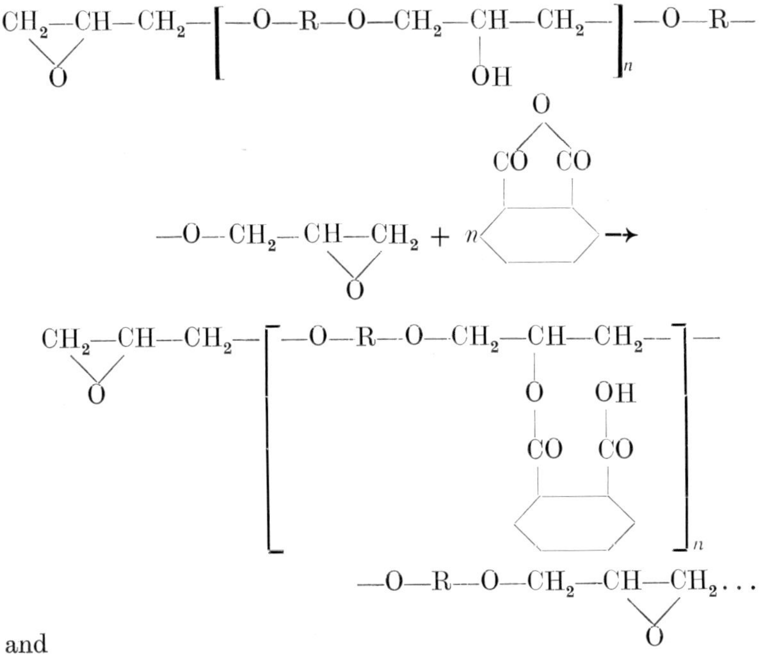

$$CH_2-CH-CH_2-\left[-O-R-O-CH_2-CH-CH_2-\right]_n-O-R-$$

(epoxide O on first group; OH on middle group)

$$-O-CH_2-CH-CH_2 + n\ \overset{O}{\underset{CO\ \ CO}{\triangle\!\!\!\bigcirc}} \rightarrow$$

$$CH_2-CH-CH_2-\left[-O-R-O-CH_2-CH-CH_2-\right]_n$$

with O and CO—CO hexagon below; and

$$-O-R-O-CH_2-CH-CH_2\ldots$$
(epoxide O)

and

$$-CH_2-CH-CH_2\ldots$$
$$O\quad OH$$
$$CO\quad CO$$
(hexagon)

$$+\ CH_2-CH-CH_2\ldots \rightarrow$$
(epoxide O)

$$-CH_2-CH-CH_2\ldots$$
$$O\qquad O-CH_2-CH-CH_2$$
$$CO\quad CO\qquad\qquad OH$$
(hexagon)

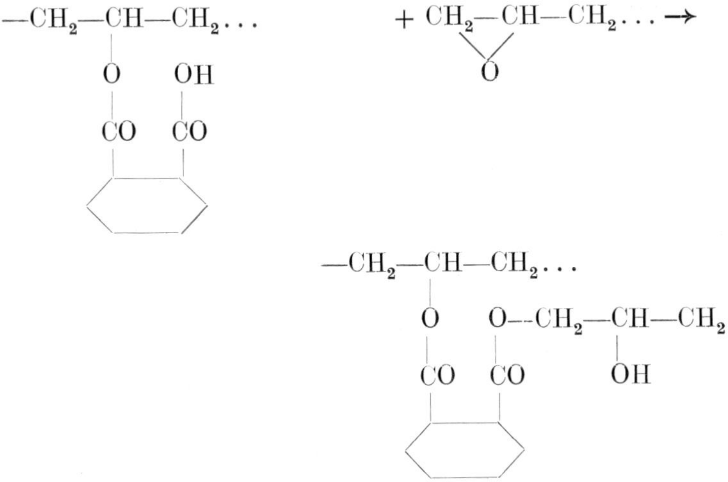

When the resin is cured with anhydrides no volatile by-products are formed [31].

Epoxy resin and maleic anhydride are both produced industrially. The process of making a material based on epoxy resin is as follows: since at room temperature epoxy resin is a viscous substance with a specific gravity between 1.15 and 1.21, while maleic anhydride is a solid crystalline substance, both components have to be heated before they can be mixed. The epoxy resin is heated to a temperature of 60—70° C, the maleic anhydride to a temperature slightly above its melting point, usually 60° C. After heating the components are thoroughly stirred together and then poured into moulds.

The amount of maleic anhydride introduced into the reaction for curing can be computed from the epoxy equivalent of the resin. The normal amount is 20—30 per cent maleic anhydride for 100 parts by weight of the mass to be prepared. The actual quantity of anhydride used depends upon the modulus of elasticity required for the material from which the model is to be made.

Curing is done in an ordinary drying oven or in a thermostatically controlled vessel. The temperature conditions and duration of the heat treatment depend upon the volume of the intended models. For small models the data on temperature conditions [32] given in Table 4 may be used.

TABLE 4.

Size of models	Soaking at 60—70 °C (hr)	Heating time to 120 °C (hr)	Soaking at 110 °C (hr)	Cooling time to 40 °C (hr)
Plates 6—8 mm thick	2	3—4	5	5
Blocks 80—150 mm in diameter and 40—120 mm thick	3—4	5—6	8—12	12

A material made with a base of epoxy resin type ED—6 satisfies the main requirements for a model material. It has comparatively high strength properties, an ultimate strength of 1300—1500 kg/cm² (18,500—21,500 lb/in.²), a proportional limit of 800—1200 kg/cm² (11,500—17,000 lb/in.²), a modulus of elasticity of

3.2–3.5 × 10⁴ kg/cm², (455,000–500,000 lb/in²), a Poisson's ratio of 0.37; when deformed it conforms to Hooke's law; it is a good dielectric, can be machined easily on normal metal-cutting machines, can be used for quite large castings of any shape, is fairly transparent after grinding and polishing so that the position of the strain gauges can be checked, and it has many other useful properties.

The main mechanical and electrical properties [30] of epoxy resins cured by amines or anhydrides are given in Tables 5 and 6.

TABLE 5. TYPICAL MECHANICAL PROPERTIES OF CURED
EPOXY RESINS

Properties	Resins cured with:	
	amines	anhydrides
Specific weight	1.19	1.2—1.23
Tensile strength (kg/cm²)	560	up to 800
Static bending strength (kg/cm²)	1500	up to 1200
Compressive strength (kg/cm²)	1300	1300
Impact strength (kg/cm²)	—	20
Water uptake in 24 hours at 20 °C (60×10×4 mm) (%)	—	0.3
Decomposition temperature (°C)	—	340
Curing shrinkage (%)	—	up to 2.3

TABLE 6. TYPICAL ELECTRICAL PROPERTIES OF CURED
EPOXY RESINS

Properties	Resins cured with:	
	amines	anhydrides
Volume resistivity (Ω · cm):		
at 25 °C	8.7×10^{14}	2.3×10^{14}
at 200 °C	1.3×10^{8}	—
Surface resistivity (Ω) at 25 °C	9.4×10^{13}	3.8×10^{13}
Dielectric constant:		
at 10³ c/s	3.8	3.65
at 10⁶ c/s	3.7	3.62
at 10¹⁰ c/s	2.8	3.01

The character of the deformation of material based on ED–6 resin with 30 per cent curing agent (maleic anhydride) shows that it can be used successfully for models intended for the investigation of strains and stresses in the elastic and elastic-plastic region under conditions of static and dynamic loads.

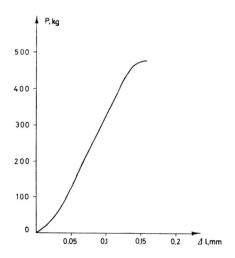

FIG. 15. Load-extension diagram of a specimen prepared from ED–6 epoxy resin and tested on an IM–4R testing machine: specimen diameter $d = 11.3$ mm, length 100 mm, $F = 1.006$ cm^2,

$$\sigma_n = \frac{450}{1.005} = 449 \text{ kg/cm}^2$$

Figure 15 gives the load-extension diagram of a specimen made from a cured epoxide material and tested on an IM–4R testing machine. It can be seen that the elongation of the specimen is directly proportional to the tensile force P. The load-extension diagram shows practically no yield plateau. Fracture occurs suddenly; the elongation and the reduction in area after rupture are found to be very small. As regards the character of the curve, it is similar to the load-extension diagrams of brittle materials such as cast iron, nickel steel, manganese steel and so on. The modulus of elasticity E, i.e. the tangent of the angle between stress curve tangent and abscissa, can be considered as constant according to the load-extension diagram (see Fig. 15).

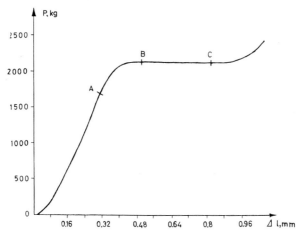

FIG. 16. Load-compression diagram of a specimen prepared from ED–6 epoxy resin and tested on a Gagarin testing machine: specimen diameter $d = 15$ mm, height $h = 45$ mm, $F = 1.76$ cm²,

$$\sigma_n = \frac{1860}{1.76} = 1056 \ \text{kg/cm}^2$$

For an investigation of the compressive strength of the material the test specimens were made in the form of short cylinders. The compression diagram for such specimens of epoxy resins (Fig. 16) is similar to that of ductile materials. When the proportional limit is exceeded, noticeable permanent deformations appear in the form of a shortening of the specimen and an increase in its diameter (Fig. 17).

Unlike the tension diagram, the compression diagram (Fig. 16) has a clearly defined section corresponding to the elastic region

(OA) and a section corresponding to the yield plateau (BC). Under a repeated loading of the specimens within the elastic range (section OA) the loading and unloading branches of the diagram correspond exactly. No permanent deformations occur, therefore, when the material is working within the elastic limit. These

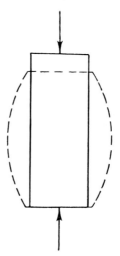

Fig. 17. Deformation of the compressed specimen

materials can therefore be recommended for models of structural elements and machine components of the most widely differing shapes and permit to investigate the character of the stress distribution in them under the most varied systems of loading and under both static and dynamic conditions.

Experimental investigations frequently call for materials with different mechanical strengths and high impact toughness and elasticity, or for materials that can be cured at lower temperatures, and so forth.

There is no great difficulty in obtaining such materials with epoxy resins. For example, to increase certain mechanical strength characteristics (compressive strength) and to bring the thermal coefficient of expansion of the resin more in line with that of metals, fillers such as aluminium oxide, cement, quartz powder, ground porcelain, etc. can be introduced into the composition. For a marked improvement in the impact toughness and elasticity, plasticizers (tricresyl phosphate, dibutyl phthalate, etc.) up to 20–25 per cent of the weight of resin are introduced. With equal quantities of resin and plasticizer the cured materials are highly elastic. In addition, the fillers mentioned have the advantage of reducing the cost of the finished models.

For the manufacture of models and specimens at room temperature (15° C and above) primary diamines or polyamines (diethylene triamine, diethylene diamine, polyethylene polyamine, etc.) can be used as curing agents. For example, a composition curing at room temperature with polyethylene polyamine may contain 92–94 per cent epoxy resin type ED–6 and 6–8 per cent polyethylene polyamine. It should be noted that with amines as curing agents the composition solidifies far more quickly than with anhydrides. In fact, the curing time at room temperature is only a few minutes.

Epoxy-resin-based materials have also the additional advantage of good adhesion to metals, ceramics, mica, porcelain and many other substances. Cements based on these resins give very strong joints between materials and are widely used in the aircraft and other industries [31]. Data on the shearing strength of various materials bonded with epoxy resin cements are given in Table 7 [30] for a test temperature of 20° C.

TABLE 7.

Material	Strength (kg/cm²)
Iron — iron	500
Chrome nickel steel — chrome nickel steel .	540
Copper — copper	500
Phosphor bronze — phosphor bronze	530
Brass — brass	450

This good adhesion between resin and metal permits the epoxy resin material of the model to be used in conjunction with the wire grids of strain gauges introduced into it. The fortunate combination of mechanical strength and good insulating and adhesive properties in cured compositions of ED–6 resin has made it possible to measure the strains and thus to investigate the stresses inside bodies of any shape with the aid of electric-resistance wire strain gauges.

10. THE MATERIAL FOR THE MODEL MOULDS

The elements and components to be investigated may be of the most varied shapes, for example, crankshafts, cross-heads, connecting-rods, rolling-contact bearing races, girders of constant and variable cross-sections, arches, cupolas, etc.

As already stated, when models are prepared, the previously weighed parts of the epoxy resin composition and of the curing agent are heated to a temperature of 70–80° C. At this temperature both the epoxy resin and the maleic anhydride are liquid. To make models from a material based on ED–6 resin it is, therefore, necessary to use moulds into which the liquid mass can be poured for curing.

Considering the low temperature of the composition when poured and the comparatively low temperature of the subsequent heat treatment the moulds can be made from cardboard, gypsum, low melting-point metals, glass or steel; the material chosen will depend upon the dimensions, the required accuracy, the shape of the model and the subsequent treatment.

Cardboard moulds

Moulds for small components and components of comparatively simple configuration, for example specimens for tensile and compressive tests, can be made from tough cardboard or heavy paper.

In order to prevent hygroscopic penetration of the epoxy resin composition, the internal surfaces of cardboard moulds are coated with a layer of silicate or rubber solution.

Plaster moulds

Moulds for large models and for models of a more complex shape with surfaces to be machined or worked with a cutting tool can be made from gypsum. Cardboard moulds are undesirable for large models, because the mass shrinks on curing and this may cause shifts of the mould, distortions, etc.

After preparation the plaster moulds are dried and their walls then lined to prevent the epoxide mass from sticking and penetrating into the body of the moulds. The mould is first lined with tough paper and then with two or three layers of tin foil. The foil is affixed with rubber solution or latex. These linings also prevent the plaster from contaminating the epoxide mass, the formation of bubbles caused by air being sucked out of the plaster walls, and bonding of the mass to the walls of the mould. After the curing process the plaster mould can easily be removed by immersion in hot water.

When cardboard and plaster moulds are used, appropriate machining allowances must be left. It should also be remembered that a moulding pattern must first be made in the shape of the future model.

Glass moulds

The use of glass moulds is recommended for flat models (plates, walls, supports and so on). The moulds are prepared from glass plate. To avoid bonding of the epoxide mass to the mould walls these are coated twice with a solution of silicone rubber in toluene and dried in a controlled-temperature oven at 80–85° C.

Metal moulds

It is slightly more difficult to make metal moulds, but when they are used the models require no subsequent machining.

Metal moulds can be used several times but they must be made in two pieces or provided with suitable pouring funnels.

As in moulds made from other materials, the epoxide mass is prevented from sticking by coating the metal surfaces with silicone compounds, waxes, polytetrafluorethylene (Ftoroplast-4), or by grinding and tin coating.

Moulds made from low melting-point metals

Moulds of this type are used for models with recesses, cavities, etc., which cannot be machined after casting. The melting point of the alloy should be within the limits of 120–130° C.

Fusible-alloy moulds enable models of any shape (hollow, slotted, etc.) to be made by the precision casting method which obviates the necessity for subsequent machining.

To remove the mould after the mass poured into it has been allowed to cure, it is immersed in transformer oil and heated to a temperature of 120–135 °C. The cured mass is a practically insoluble and unmeltable solid substance and therefore unharmed if the model is heated to 120–150° C.

A great deal of time is required for making moulds from low melting-point metals, since an exact copy of the component is required for the casting of the mould itself; these moulds should, therefore, only be used when the model has a very complex shape with surfaces inaccessible for machining.

In all cases attention must be paid to the soundness of the moulds, as the heated liquid epoxide mass has a low viscosity and can easily penetrate gypsum, cardboard and similar materials.

11. RECOMMENDATIONS FOR THE MACHINING OF MODELS AND SPECIMENS

A material based on epoxy resins can easily be machined and worked with ordinary cutting tools. It lends itself to turning, milling, planing, drilling, grinding and other forms of mechanical treatment.

When machining the models it is essential to use a sharp tool and to remove only thin shavings (0.5–1 mm thick) at moderate speed and pressure. The thickness of the layer removed during finish machining should not exceed 0.15–0.5 mm.

The cutters should be sharpened in the same way as for finishing tough materials. They must always be kept sharp, since a blunt tool frequently causes chipping at the edges of the model, particularly when a thick layer is removed.

The strength of the cured epoxide mass permits machining of a great variety of members (nuts, bolts, disks, washers, etc.). With models in the form of disks, rings and cylinders with internal bores it is desirable to finish the outer surface first and then to bore the hole. Grooves and recessed connections should be end milled.

Holes should be drilled with a small diameter at first, then gradually enlarged by successive cuts with drills of larger diameter or end milling cutters. Large circular holes are best bored on a lathe.

Straight surfaces can be machined either by side or end milling. Planing machines can be used for machining flat surfaces, but planing is much slower than milling because the milling chip can be allowed to reach a thickness of 2.5 mm, which on a planer would lead to chipping.

Irregular or complicated shapes are machined most simply by spiral milling cutters or rotary files. The use of a rotary file is a very convenient form of machining and considerably quicker than hand working.

To avoid cracking and warping of models having thin elements, the use of coolant (water, light oil, solution of sodium bicarbonate in water) is recommended during machining.

The fineness of the required surface finish depends on the character of the problem to be solved. For contact problems the models must be prepared very carefully, since the presence of various surface irregularities (micro-irregularities) can have a substantial influence on the distribution of the stresses at internal points. Their influence is particularly great at points close to the contact surface. Hence, for this type of problem the working surfaces of the models must be ground and sometimes also polished.

When direct stresses, for example in bent or stretched members, are measured, the faces of the components need not be machined so carefully.

The surface of the models can be ground on grinding machines or with simple devices such as emery cloth stretched over a plate of mirror glass. Manual grinding is carried out dry, machine grinding requires a coolant.

Models can be polished on a normal polishing machine with a rotating metal disk covered with felt and GOI paste; polishing can also be done by hand.

If for any reason it is necessary to pass light through the model to check the position of strain gauges, a coat of varnish or a layer of oil can be applied.

12. UNBONDED WIRE STRAIN GAUGES

Wire strain gauges on a paper base consist structurally of layers of paper and adhesive.

When a method for the electrical measurement of strains inside a component was worked out, it was found necessary to develop a new design of wire strain gauges that would satisfy the following main requirements:

(1) the relative change in resistance of the gauge should be proportional to the measured strain;

(2) the strain gauges should reflect without distortion the actual character of the phenomena under investigation;

(3) a strain gauge placed inside the testpiece should not act as a foreign body destroying or altering the elastic characteristics of the material of the testpiece.

The gauge should satisfy certain other requirements as well: its dimensions should be convenient for handling, it should have a sufficiently high resistance, and so forth.

The first main requirement is satisfied in practice wherever the wire of the gauge is working within the elastic range.

To reflect fully the character of the phenomena under investigation (second requirement), the strain gauge must undergo precisely the same deformations as the section in which it is placed. For the measurement of surface strains the strain gauge is affixed to the surface of the testpiece with a special adhesive ensuring that the surface and the wire grid of the gauge are strained together.

The third condition applies specially to strain gauges intended for the measurement of stresses inside components. On the surfaces of components, strain gauges of practically any size and configuration can be used without upsetting the structure of the material and hence without changing the direction of the lines of force inside the entire volume of the component including its surface layers. However, if an element made from a material

FIG. 18. Fractures of specimens with
internal paper-based strain gauges

with different strength characteristics from those of the basic material is introduced into the inner layers, quite a different phenomenon is observed.

As is known, wire strain gauges are prepared by placing a wire grid on a carrier of paper and some type of cement [Fig. 10 (a)]; some strain gauges are also carried on a film of BF−2. The practical application of such bonded strain gauges to the investigation of internal stresses has shown that they are unsuitable for plane or three-dimensional internal states of stress. They can only be used for the investigation of linear stresses when the direction of the lines of force coincides with that of the wire grid.

The character of the rupture of specimens with internal paper-based strain gauges is shown in Fig. 18. The rupture took place in the plane of the bonded strain gauge; this confirms the discussed necessity of making special internal unbonded strain gauges which do not form a foreign inclusion in the material of the testpiece.

For the measurement of internal stresses, therefore, the good adhesion between materials based on ED−6 resin and metals or other materials was utilised. As a check, the bond between two specimens of epoxy-based material was tested with good results.

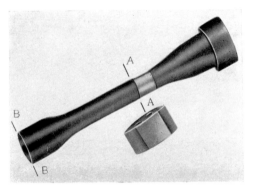

FIG. 19. Fracture of a specimen
prepared in two stages

Figure 19 shows a testpiece made in two stages. An already finished cylinder of ED−6 material was placed back into the mould and liquid epoxide mass ED−6 was poured over it; after curing, the specimen was again machined and subjected to a tensile test on an IM−4R testing machine. The result was close to the maximum stress observed in tests on specimens made in a single stage (tensile strength 900 kg/cm² or 12,800 lb/in²) and the rupture did not take place at the "joint" (section AA), as can be seen from Fig. 19, but across a wider section of the specimen (section BB). The method of preparing unbonded strain gauges was thus developed on the basis of the good adhesive property of resin ED−6.

The process of making the strain gauges is as follows. A temporary base is made for the strain gauge: a foil of ED−6 resin-based material with a width equal to the grid length of the gauge, a thickness of 0.1–0.15 mm, and a length of 10–12 mm. This foil 1 is glued with BF–2 cement to a U-shaped cardboard frame 2 at the points A and B [Fig. 20 (a)]. After the cement has set a cut D is made in the frame so that the turns of the wire grid can be wound without obstruction.

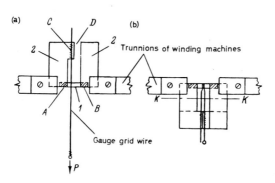

FIG. 20. Jig for the manufacture of
unbonded wire strain gauges

First of all a "blank" for the future grid of the gauge is made in the form of a single strand of high-resistance wire with the terminal leads of copper wire 0.10–0.15 mm diameter welded on (see Fig. 27). The length of the strand depends upon the grid length and the number of turns of the gauge grid to be wound.

One terminal copper lead is fixed (cemented) to the cardboard frame at C. Then the temporary frame is mounted in the trunnions of the winding machine (see Fig. 22) which is used to wind the turns of the wire grid onto the foil 1; finally the other terminal lead is fixed (cemented) to the frame. The finished form of the gauge mounted on its temporary base is shown in Fig. 20 (b).

During the winding of the turns the wire must be kept at a constant tension. The distances between the individual turns of the grid are set with the aid of a scale grating in the eyepiece of a microscope which is provided on the machine.

The cardboard frame thus enables the grid of the gauge to be wound onto the temporary base without the use of adhesive to secure it; moreover, the wire is kept permanently taut. A group of strain gauges made on the temporary base is hung into a mould, and epoxide mass is poured in up to the level K–K [Fig. 20 (b)]. After the resin has been allowed to cure, the

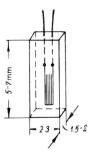

FIG. 21. General view of an unbonded wire strain gauge

cardboard frame is removed mechanically and the gauge is in the form shown in Fig. 21.

The base length of the strain gauges can be from 0.5 to 5 mm depending upon the type of stresses to be investigated. The wire grid consists of 7 to 10 turns covering a width of 0.2–0.3 mm. The linear dimensions of these gauges (for example with a base length of 0.5–1.0 mm) make it possible in practice to measure stresses at individual points. The resistance of strain gauges made in this way ranges from 70 to 200 Ω.

It has been shown in practice that the sensitivity of internal wire strain gauges with a gauge length of 1.0–2.0 mm is sufficient for measurements with ordinary strain measuring devices recording the results on MPO–2 electro-magnetic mirror oscillographs with galvo elements of type I and II.

The gauge factor of unbonded strain gauges made of nichrome wire with a resistance of 3500–4000 Ω/m is 1.5 to 1.7.

The possibility of producing strain gauges with a gauge length of 0.5–2 mm permits investigation of localized and contact stresses under both static and dynamic loading conditions. The strain gauges are placed in the moulds of the models and epoxide mass is poured in. As a result of the good adhesive properties of the epoxy resin, the gauges form a continuous part of the body of the cured model and the wire grid is found to be mounted inside the testpiece.

The described technique of making wire strain gauges permits introduction of the unbonded grid of a strain gauge right into the volume of a model without upsetting the continuity and homogeneity of the material from which the model is made; this is not only expedient but absolutely essential for an investigation of the internal stresses in a complex (plane or three-dimensional) state of stress.

13. DEVICES FOR PRODUCING UNBONDED STRAIN GAUGES

Unbonded wire strain gauges are produced with the aid of a hand-operated winding machine and a device for welding the gauge wire to the terminal leads. A brief description now follows.

Winding machine for strain gauge grids

The grids are usually made on machines of widely varying design by placing a constantan or other high-resistance wire of 0.015–0.035 mm diameter in loops between two parallel rows of needles. The distance between the two rows of needles is equal to the required grid length of the strain gauge. In practice, the diameter of the needles, which determines the distance between the turns, cannot be made less than 0.2 mm, and the grid length cannot be less than 2.0 mm.

Since strain gauges must have a certain resistance (not less than 50–80 Ω), a small grid length of less than 5 mm requires a corresponding increase in width. For example, strain gauges with a grid length of 2 mm have a width of 15–30 mm. Because of the small difference in longitudinal and transverse length of the turns, such strain gauges have a high cross-sensitivity factor.

It is therefore not possible to use existing strain gauges for measuring the magnitude of stress concentrations and contact stresses in working components and members, or in models of them, in plane and three-dimensional states of stress. Neither can they be used for electrical strain-gauge measurements of the magnitude of internal stresses by the method suggested here. Investigations of this type are possible only if unbonded strain gauges are available, or more precisely unbonded micro strain gauges with a short gauge length.

A simple machine (Fig. 22) has therefore been designed and built for the preparation of unbonded strain gauges. It consists of the following six main units: base with holder, frame, drive mechanism, wire tensioning device, micrometer screw and MIR—12 microscope.

The base 1 and holder 2 support the winding jig and hold the microscope in its working position.

The frame consists of a metal plate 14 on which are mounted an attachment for tensioning the grid wire during winding, a fixed bracket 12 and a movable bracket 19 which slides along the guide 20 and can be locked by the screws 21. A viewing mirror 18 is fixed to the plate 14 between the brackets 12 and 19.

The drive mechanism consists of a set of gear wheels 10 and 22. Between the trunnions 8 is fixed the foil 9 on which the wire grid is wound; this foil is turned by means of the handle 3. The foil, or the temporary cardboard frame with the foil, is placed in the axis of the trunnions and clamped by screws with washers. The lower right-hand gearwheel is movable so that the distance between trunnions can be adjusted if necessary.

The wire tensioning device is fixed to the plate 14 by means of a screw and can be moved sideways in either direction. Its axle carries a drum 15 over which passes a loaded filament 16 fixed to the terminal lead of the grid. The load holds the grid wire in constant tension. The axle of the tensioning device can

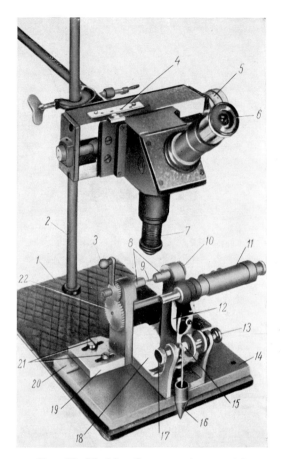

FIG. 22. Machine for preparing special
wire grids

be removed or placed in position by screwing or unscrewing the
locking pins 13 and 17.

A micrometer screw is fitted for adjusting the pitch between
turns. In this device a micrometer screw 11, type MR, with a
scale division of 0.002 mm is used. A groove at the end of the
movable stem of the screw guides the grid wire during the
winding of the turns.

4

The microscope assists in winding the turns accurately with gaps of 0.010–0.015 mm between wires. A microscope type MIR–12 is used in this instrument and fixed to the stand before winding. If transparent foils of dielectric material are used, the reflection from the mirror provides a good view of the wire turns in the microscope, which gives an upright image and is focussed by turning the objective 7 with the lower knurled ring and clamping it in position by a lock nut. The eyepiece 6 has a scale grating which is set parallel to the turns and perpendicular to the edge of the foil during winding. A micrometer screw serves to move the microscope parallel with the foil through a distance of up to 50 mm. Integer millimetres are read off the millimetre scale 4 fixed to the top of the microscope slide, tenths and hundredths of a millimetre are read off the drum 5 with a scale division of 0.01 mm. The field of view of the microscope has a width of 5 mm.

This machine can be used for making short gauge-length strain gauges on a paper base with a two-layer wire grid [see Fig. 10 (b)]. When the grids are wound on a paper base, a reel of wire is placed on the axle of the tensioning device.

The machine has been used to produce wire strain gauges of several different sizes from both nichrome and constantan wire of 0.015–0.018 mm diameter with 7 to 10 turns and a distance of 0.03 mm between the centres of the turns. The width of the gauges was not more than 0.2–0.3 mm and the gauge length 0.5–5 mm and over. A check on strain gauges of these dimensions gave satisfactory results.

It has been proved by experiment that for the measurement of stress concentrations it is best to make strain gauges with a length of 2 mm and a width of 0.25 mm. With nichrome wire of 0.018 mm diameter, their resistance is 90–100 Ω, which is fully acceptable for ordinary electrical strain-measuring apparatus.

Devices for welding the terminal leads

In the manufacture of wire strain gauges the terminal leads of the grid are either soldered or welded on. They cannot be soldered to the grid wire of the micro strain gauges cast in

models made from an epoxide mass, because the various tin
soldering alloys do not give a strong joint between solder and
epoxide mass due to the poor adhesion between the resin and tin.

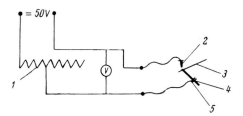

FIG. 23. Circuit of an electric spark
welding device

Hence in the manufacture of wire strain gauges intended for
the study of internal stresses, the leads have to be welded to the
grid wire. Two forms of welding can be employed: spark welding
or resistance welding.

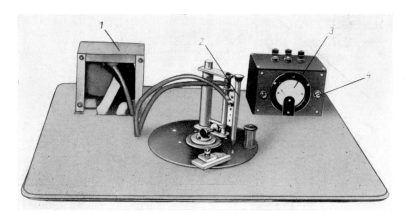

FIG. 24. Equipment for resistance welding

Spark welding can be carried out with very simple equipment.
The circuit of a device for spark welding is shown in Fig. 23.
A rectifier gives a d.c. supply and a rheostat 1 controls the volt-
age at the contacts. The d.c. supply voltage is selected by

4*

experiment and depends on the diameter and material of the wire to be welded. For welding copper and constantan wires the authors used 25–30 V.

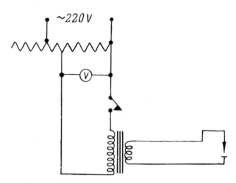

FIG. 25. Electrical circuit for resistance welding

The order in which the work is carried out is as follows. The terminal lead (a length of copper wire 4 of 0.10–0.15 mm dia.) is placed in the clamp 5 connected to one side of the supply

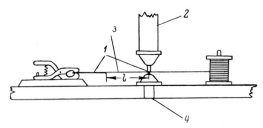

FIG. 26. Arrangement of wires between
welding contacts:

1: terminals; 2: upper contact; 3: grid wire; 4: lower
contact, l length of wire in the gauge

system. The other side is connected to a graphite pencil 2. After the end of the grid wire 3 has been properly placed on the lead 4, the tip of the graphite pencil is brought into the welding position. A spark is discharged when this is done and welds the wires, the constantan or nichrome wire being fused on with a globule of copper.

A disadvantage of this method of welding is the difficulty of accurate positioning and welding of the grid wire to the terminal lead, which gives rise to an additional scatter in the resistance value of the strain gauges. For this reason resistance welding has been used in the manufacture of the small wire strain gauges.

The equipment for resistance welding, shown in a general view in Fig. 24, has the following main parts: an autotransformer

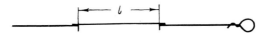

FIG. 27. "Blank" for short gauge-length
wire strain gauges

(type LATR–1), a welding transformer 1, a contact switch 4, a voltmeter 3 and a clamping device 2 for the parts to be welded. The circuit is illustrated in Fig. 25.

The current required for welding wires of different diameter was selected by varying the voltage in the primary of the welding transformer. When making short base-length strain gauges with nichrome wire of 0.015–0.018 mm dia., it was 130–140 V in the primary. To prevent the wires from sticking to the contacts, the lower contact was made of copper and the upper one of tungsten.

A diagram of the device for welding the leads to the grid wire is given in Fig. 26. The completed "blank" for the strain gauge grid has the form shown in Fig. 27.

14. MOUNTING OF THE STRAIN GAUGES IN THE MOULDS

Mounting the strain gauges in the moulds is an important operation in the production of the models. The final accuracy of the data obtained from the models under load will depend on the accuracy with which the strain gauges are installed in relation to each other at the required points or sections and also on how accurately their axes are orientated in the required directions. Therefore, after preparing the mould of the model it is necessary to draw up a scheme for the positioning of the strain gauges and their attachment to one or two internal surfaces of the mould, taking into consideration the allowances required for the further treatment of the model.

During curing the model shrinks and its surfaces may have slopes, curves and hollows. For an accurate determination of the position of the strain gauges inside the model, it is therefore desirable to attach positional reference markers directly to the strain gauges and not to the walls of the mould, particularly in models for three-dimensional investigations.

When a small number of strain gauges is installed (3–5) they can be mounted separately (with separate terminal leads); a large number may be mounted in a joint arrangement (Fig. 29).

The finished strain gauge (Fig. 21) has copper wire leads 10–15 mm long. For installation, these leads are welded to conductor leads of the required length.

The introduction of a large number of leads into the cured epoxide mass will reinforce it to a certain extent, which could affect the accuracy of the data obtained. To prevent any substantial influence of the leads on the accuracy of the measurements, it is essential first that the strength characteristics of the lead wire should be approximately the same as those of the cured epoxide mass and, secondly, that the diameter of the conductor leads should be as small as possible. In the experiments discussed below the material for these conductors was soft copper wire 0.10–0.15 mm in diameter.

To reduce further the influence of the strain gauge leads on the results of the measurements, some attempt must be made to place them in regions of the model which are not adjacent to the points of application of the experimental loads.

After the model has been machined, the conductor leads emerging from the surface of the model at various points (sections) must be soldered to the circuit wires leading to the measuring equipment. Since the cross-sectional area at the ends of the conductor leads (with a diameter of 0.10–0.15 mm) is very small, it is practically impossible to make soldered joints without damaging the surface of the model.

To avoid such damage during soldering, it is expedient to thicken the conductor leads where they emerge from the surface of the model. For this purpose short lengths of soft copper wire of 1 mm dia. are welded to the ends of the internal conductor

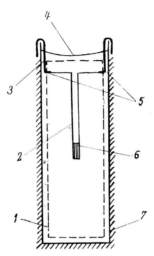

Fig. 28. Arrangement for mounting a single strain gauge:

1: outline of finished specimen; 2: copper wire $d = 0.1-0.15$ mm; 3: thickened terminals made from copper wire $d = 1$ mm; 4: level of liquid epoxy resin; 5: positions of joints to be soldered; 6: wire strain gauge; 7: internal wall of mould

leads; their length is chosen so that after the model has been machined, a length of 2–3 mm of this wire remains in the body of the model. If this is done, soldering of the circuit leads to the measuring equipment presents no difficulty.

If possible, the places where the leads emerge from the surface of the model should be a fair distance from the position of the strain gauges; this is particularly important for strain gauges located near the surface.

Figure 28 shows one way of mounting a single wire strain gauge inside a cylindrical specimen prepared for compression tests on cured epoxide resin. Figure 29 shows the arrangement for a group of strain gauges to be used for an investigation of the plane state of stress in a plate with a central circular hole.

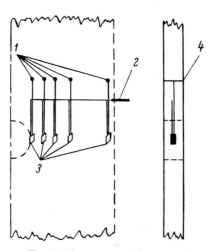

Fig. 29. Arrangement for mounting a group of strain gauges:

1: individual leads; 2: common lead; 3: strain gauges; 4: position of soldered joints with leads to the measuring equipment

The installation arrangement for an investigation of the stresses in three-dimensional models is rather complicated, because not less than six gauges are required to find the directions of the principal planes and the magnitude of the stresses acting on them. Thus, in order to find the state of stress at a point inside a body if the positions of the principal planes are unknown, groups of individual strain gauges must be mounted together.

There are two methods of solving this problem. In the first, multi-gauge rosettes are prepared (two, three and six gauges) and placed at the internal points to be studied. With this method, the required number of strain gauges must be installed at each of these points in the specified orientations. This solution can be applied if the models of components and members have a complex shape. Its disadvantage is that if one of the strain gauges fails, it is not possible to use the remaining five to determine the direction of the principal planes and the other characteristics of the state of stress at the investigated point.

In the second method, separate groups of strain gauges, with their axes all in the same direction are installed, and in each individual group this direction corresponds to one of the directions of a six-gauge rosette. This solution can be applied if the models have a constant profile over their entire length (long components of constant cross-section). A great advantage of installing the strain gauges in this second manner is that failure of a single gauge does not affect the solution of the problem as a whole; for with this method the overall strain distribution can be built up from the readings of a number of strain gauges that have their axes all in the same direction and are all located in one and the same section. The readings missed as a result of the failure of one gauge can be determined by interpolating the data obtained from the other strain gauges in the same group.

If the models or structural members have a very complicated shape, then one must resort to casting several models in which the strain gauges are mounted at exactly the same points but in different directions.

When installing the strain gauges in the mould, consideration should be given to the number of measurements to be taken. One and the same installation of strain gauges may serve to investigate several variations in the outlines or dimensions of a model. For example, when the most rational cross-sections or outlines of a component are to be found there is no need to prepare several similar models (with slightly different outlines).

Experiments can be carried out on one and the same model, provided that initially the strain gauges have been installed in such a way that each time a change is made in the configuration of the model, strain gauges are again located at the required points of the particular section to be studied. Strain gauges located near a surface to be altered may be removed together with the layer that is machined away, but the next strain gauge should then be located at such a distance from the first gauge removed that after machining it occupies the position previously occupied by the removed gauge.

This method of installing strain gauges was applied to measurements of the stress in a plate with a central hole (see Section 19). Strain gauge 1 (Fig. 40), which was used for a hole of 10 mm dia., was removed for the second measurement with the hole drilled to 16 mm dia., and its place was taken by strain gauge 2.

For an investigation of stresses at various depths below a surface, a strain gauge placed initially at a great depth inside the body of the model can be gradually brought closer to the surface during tests by the successive removal of layers of material from the model. Such an arrangement was used for the study of contact stresses (see Section 20).

15. GAUGE CALIBRATION

The ordinary, widely used electrical strain measuring equipment is designed for wire strain gauges with a resistance of $50-80\ \Omega$ and over. The unbonded strain gauges already described are intended to be used with such an equipment.

Since the total length of wire in the grid of an unbonded strain gauge (made, for example, with a gauge length of 2 mm) is $8-10$ times less than the length of wire in the grid of an ordinary strain gauge, the wire used in unbonded strain gauges must have a comparatively high resistance (of the order of $3500\ \Omega/\text{m}$ and over, at a diameter of $12-18\ \mu$) in order to give a gauge with a sufficiently high resistance. A single millimetre of this wire has a resistance of about $4\ \Omega$.

If the wire of the gauge grid is nominally $24-30$ mm long, its actual length may vary in resistance by up to $3-4\ \Omega$ for a total resistance of $90-120\ \Omega$.

It is well known that this variation in resistance, which is always present to a certain degree in gauges (and to a greater extent in gauges with a short base length), considerably complicates the measurements, from the initial balancing of the bridge circuit to the final analysis of the data obtained. The variation is particularly undesirable in a group of strain gauges placed in a single model or in identical models intended to give comparable results. Hence, it is most desirable to employ strain gauges of equal resistance for the investigation of the stresses in any one model since this considerably speeds up data processing; otherwise it is necessary to prepare calibration gauges for each group of measuring gauges.

To obtain a smaller spread of resistance values it is best to produce strain gauges in large batches (100–200 at a time) with subsequent grouping according to resistance values.

The method of calibrating the gauges depends upon the form of the stresses in the testpiece. In some cases it is possible to calibrate the active gauges directly, in others special calibration specimens have to be made.

Direct calibration of the active gauges is possible if the loading system or the shape of the component can be altered in such a way that the stresses at the points considered can be determined comparatively easily by calculation. In this case, a calibration with known loads is carried out by comparing the calculated stresses (strains) with the readings of the recording instruments.

Such a system of calibration was used, for example, in measuring the stresses in the region of stress concentration in a plate with a central circular hole (see Section 19). There, the strain gauges were calibrated as follows: the plate without the hole was cast with a group of strain gauges of equal resistance placed at the required points. After machining to the required dimensions the undrilled plate was placed in a testing machine and stretched under loads from 50 to 250 kg. The readings of each strain gauge under these were recorded on a recording instrument. Once the cross-sectional area of the undrilled plate, the value of the applied force and the readings of the recording instrument for each strain gauge were known, the value of each scale division could be determined in kg/cm^2 and in unit strain.

A similar method can be used for many other cases of stress concentrations with a linear or plane state of stress. This method of calibrating strain gauges embedded in members is very reliable and convenient since it does not require the preparation of calibration specimens.

Special calibration specimens are needed, however, for investigations of three-dimensional stresses. In this case, at the same

FIG. 30. Calibration specimens

time as the model to be investigated is cast with its group of strain gauges, several small cylindrical moulds with gauges of equal resistance are also cast, and from these the calibration specimens are subsequently prepared (Fig. 30). Calibration is carried out by either compressing or stretching these specimens.

Since in the experimental investigation of internal stresses with the aid of wire strain gauges, the strains are measured directly, the scale divisions of the measuring instrument must be calibrated in terms of strain values.

The value of a scale division of the measuring instrument for static loads is determined in the following way: the cylindrical calibration specimens with the embedded wire strain gauges are machined to the specified dimensions. The authors have used cylinders 40 mm high and 15 mm dia. or tensile specimens of 10 mm dia. The calibration specimens are subjected to tension or compression on a testing machine and readings of the strain gauge signals are taken. It is known from the theory of strength of materials that the strain ε is

$$\varepsilon = \frac{P}{EF}.$$

If the strain ε is determined for a known load P, the known cross-sectional area F and the known modulus of elasticity E, and a reading N is taken under the given load P, the strain per scale division is defined as

$$C = \frac{\varepsilon}{N}.$$

Table 8 gives an example of a calibration from the readings of three specimens under static loads from 100 to 500 kg.

TABLE 8.

Compression (kg)	Reading in pressures $N_{av.}$	$\varepsilon = \dfrac{P}{EF} \times 10^5$	$C = \dfrac{\varepsilon}{N_{av.}} \times 10^5$
100	105	158.714	1.512
200	210	317.457	1.512
300	315	476.171	1.512
400	420	634.914	1.512
500	525	793.628	1.512

Note: $E = 3.5 \times 10^4$ kg/cm²; $F = 1.8$ cm²

16. EVALUATION OF THE STRESSES IN COMPONENTS FROM DATA OBTAINED BY MODEL TESTS

When the internal stresses are determined by strain measurement with unbonded wire strain gauges, the question arises how the stresses obtained from the models can be converted into stresses in the actual objects under investigation. In solving this question two cases must be examined.

In certain problems the strained state is not dependent upon the elastic constants of the material; data obtained from measurements on models can then be transferred to the actual component by the rules of geometrical similarity and similarity of the forces. Such problems include, for example, the plane states of stress with statically determinate external loads, simply-connected cross-sections and absence of body forces.

In other problems the transfer of the model data to the actual component depends upon the elastic constants of the materials of both the model and the component. In this case special techniques are needed: the measurement of dislocation strains and the testing of models with different Poisson's ratios.

Efforts should be made to prepare the models from materials having the same elastic characteristics as the materials of the components being studied. Thus, small components and members made from plastics can be made to actual size and tested under laboratory or industrial conditions. In investigations of the state of stress in such plastics components the strain measurements can be carried out on the components directly.

The main question arising when experimental results are transferred from a model made of plastics to a component made of a structural material such as steel, is the influence exerted by the material itself on the stress distribution.

Well known proofs [14, 33, 4] exist that the stress distribution in a plane state of stress is independent of the physical constants of the material provided the material is homogeneous and isotropic, body forces are either absent or constant and the material is working within the elastic limit. For example, in a plane state of stress under certain limiting conditions [34, 35] the stress distribution in an elastic body is independent of the elastic constants of the material of the body. The proof follows directly from an examination of the equations:

$$\frac{\partial \sigma_x}{\partial x} + \frac{\partial \tau_{xy}}{\partial y} + X = 0,$$

$$\frac{\partial \sigma_x}{\partial y} + \frac{\partial \tau_{xy}}{\partial x} + Y = 0,$$

$$\nabla^2 (\sigma_x + \sigma_y) = 0 \quad \left(\Delta^2 = \frac{\partial^2}{\partial x^2} + \frac{\partial^2}{\partial y^2} \right).$$

The state of stress is completely defined by integration of these equations and introduction of the given boundary conditions

$$\sigma_x \cos(xv) + \tau_{xy} \cos(yv) = x;$$

$$\tau_{xy} \cos(xv) + \sigma_y \cdot \cos(yv) = y.$$

It is seen that the elastic constants do not enter these equations when the body forces X, Y are constant.

However, this is valid only if the plane region of the elastic body is simply-connected. In the case of a multiply-connected region, the external forces applied to each closed contour bounding the investigated region must be individually balanced or form a couple [34].

Consequently, if the external forces are statically determinate, if the body forces (X, Y) are either absent or constant, and if the plane region of the elastic body is simply connected (or in the case of a multiply-connected region the external forces are individually balanced or form a couple), then the stresses in the component under investigation can be expressed in terms of the stresses in the loaded model regardless of the elastic constants of the model and actual component:

$$\sigma = \sigma_m \frac{\beta \, d_m}{\alpha \, d},$$

where σ is the stress at an arbitrary point in the component (i.e. any of the stresses σ_x, σ_y or τ_{xy}), σ_m is the stress at the analogous point in the model, d and d_m are the thicknesses of the component and model respectively, and α and β are the factors of geometrical similarity and similarity of the forces,

$$\alpha = \frac{\lambda}{\lambda_m} \quad \text{and} \quad \beta = \frac{P}{P_m} = \frac{q}{q_m},$$

where λ is an arbitrary reference length within the limits of the component under investigation, λ_m is the corresponding length in the loaded model, P is any of the forces acting on the surface of the component, P_m is the corresponding force acting on the surface of the model, q is the intensity of any of the distributed loads acting on the surface of the component, and q_m is the intensity of the corresponding distributed load on the model.

If it is assumed that body forces exist and are an arbitrary function of the coordinates, then the stresses will always depend on the elastic constants, even in the case of the plane state of stress. This follows from the fact that the third equation of the plane stress system then takes another form and includes Poisson's ratio.

As Proshko has pointed out [35], this problem has no great practical significance, since even if constant body forces exist, e.g. forces of gravity, the stresses due to the weight of a model of normal dimensions are very small in comparison with the stresses caused by a surface load.

If the investigated plane region of the elastic body is multiply-connected and the external forces applied to any closed contour bounding this region are not individually balanced, then the stresses also depend on the elastic coefficients. A general solution for the stresses is then found by investigating a geometrically similar model and subsequently applying corrective terms in the solution depending upon the elastic coefficients. These corrective terms can be determined experimentally by testing a number of suitable models with and without dislocation strains [14].

Since great difficulties are encountered in carrying out such experiments, Lyakhnitskii has established that for a number of cases it is sufficient to carry out an experimental stress analysis on two models that must be made of materials with different Poisson's ratios μ but may have any factors of similarity [36]. The stresses in the investigated component are then defined by

$$\sigma = \frac{1}{d} \left[\sigma_1 \frac{d_1 \beta_1 (\mu - \mu_2)}{\alpha_1 (\mu_1 - \mu_2)} - \sigma_2 \frac{d_2 \beta_2 (\mu - \mu_1)}{\alpha_2 (\mu_1 - \mu_2)} \right],$$

where the notation is as before, the quantities without subscripts refer to the actual component and the subscripts denote the number of the model. If both models are identical in size and identically loaded, this equation is reduced to

$$\sigma = \frac{d_m \, \beta}{d \, \alpha} \left[\sigma_1 \, \frac{\mu - \mu_2}{\mu_1 - \mu_2} - \sigma_2 \, \frac{\mu - \mu_1}{\mu_1 - \mu_2} \right].$$

The experiments can easily be carried out by the electric wire strain-gauge method of measurement, because identical models with built-in wire strain gauges can be prepared from materials with different elastic characteristics, for example Bakelite with $\mu = 0.25$ and epoxide mass with $\mu = 0.36$.

In a three-dimensional state of stress, the stress distribution depends upon Poisson's ratio of the material, even for statically determinate problems, simply-connected regions and in the absence of body forces [35]. This can be seen from the nine differential equations defining the state of stress at a point.

Many authors have pointed out the insignificant influence exerted by Poisson's ratio on the state of stress, but to be certain that the result obtained is accurate, the influence of Poisson's ratio must be included in the calculations, especially for problems that have no theoretical solution.

If it is assumed that the region investigated in a three-dimensional problem is simply-connected (no cavities or holes), that there are no body forces and that the boundary conditions ensure statical determinacy of the forces, then the stresses obtained in models can be converted into stresses in the actual component by experiments with geometrically similar models made from materials with different Poisson's ratios.

Stresses in models geometrically similar to the actual component and loaded similarly but with different Poisson's ratios can be determined from the following formulae [35]:

$$\sigma_i = \frac{P_{ni}}{\lambda_{ni}^2} \cdot \frac{\varphi_1 + \mu_i \, \varphi_2}{\varphi_3 + \mu_i} \quad (i = 1, 2, 3),$$

where i is the number of the model, φ_1, φ_2, φ_3 are unknown functions which can be found experimentally by determining the stresses in three different models, μ is Poisson's ratio,

$$P_{ni} = \frac{P_n}{\beta_i} \text{ and } \lambda_{ni} = \frac{\lambda_n}{\alpha_i} \ (i = 1, 2, 3),$$

where P_n denotes the forces acting on the actual component, P_{ni} denotes the corresponding forces acting on the models, α_i denotes the coefficients of geometrical similarity and β_i denotes the coefficients of similarity of the forces.

Substituting in this formula for σ_i the given conditions of similarity and eliminating the unknown functions φ, we obtain an expression which even in the most general case permits the stress σ in an actual component to be expressed in terms of the stresses, elastic constants and factors of similarity of three models:

$$\sigma = \frac{\beta_1 \sigma_1 (\mu_2 - \mu)(\mu_1 - \mu_3)(\alpha_2^2 \beta_3 \sigma_3 - \alpha_3^2 \beta_2 \sigma_2) -}{\alpha_1^2 \alpha_2^2 \beta_3 \sigma_3 (\mu_1 - \mu_2)(\mu_3 - \mu) +}$$
$$\frac{- \beta_2 \sigma_2 (\mu_1 - \mu)(\mu_2 - \mu_3)(\alpha_1^2 \beta_3 \sigma_3 - \alpha_3^2 \beta_1 \sigma_1)}{+ \alpha_2^2 \alpha_3^2 \beta_1 \sigma_1 (\mu_2 - \mu_3)(\mu_1 - \mu) + \alpha_3^2 \alpha_1^2 \beta_2 \sigma_2 (\mu_3 - \mu_1)(\mu_2 - \mu)}.$$

If the three models are geometrically identical and identically loaded, i.e. if

$$\alpha_1 = \alpha_2 = \alpha_3 = \alpha \text{ and } \beta_1 = \beta_2 = \beta_3 = \beta,$$

then the formula takes the form

$$\sigma = \frac{\beta}{\alpha^2} \frac{\sigma_1 (\mu_2 - \mu)(\mu_1 - \mu_3)(\sigma_3 - \sigma_2) - \sigma_2 (\mu_1 - \mu)(\mu_2 - \mu_3)(\sigma_3 - \sigma_1)}{\sigma_3 (\mu_1 - \mu_2)(\mu_3 - \mu) + \sigma_1 (\mu_2 - \mu_3)(\mu_1 - \mu) + \sigma_2 (\mu_3 - \mu_1)(\mu_2 - \mu)}.$$

If Poisson's ratios of the materials of model and actual component are equal, i.e. $\mu_1 = \mu$, then the stresses in the actual component can be determined by testing one model only. In this case, the last expression takes the form

$$\sigma = \frac{\beta_1 \sigma_1}{\alpha_1^2}.$$

This formula coincides with the expression found for the

stresses in the plane problem when the stress distribution is not dependent upon Poisson's ratio.

It is seen that great experimental difficulties are involved in determining the influence of Poisson's ratio in the solution of three-dimensional as well as certain plane problems; it is therefore very desirable to conduct experiments on a single model made from a material with the same Poisson's ratio as the material of the actual component. The properties of materials based on epoxy resins, described in Section 9, make it possible to produce materials with the Poisson's ratio required for solving the most varied three-dimensional and plane problems, because different quantities of curingagent and various fillers and plasticizers can be introduced into their composition.

CHAPTER III

EXPERIMENTAL STUDY OF INTERNAL STRESSES UNDER STATIC LOADING

To PROVIDE an experimental basis for the described technique of measuring internal stresses in components, work was carried out on the experimental solution of a number of problems involving internal stresses.

Some of these problems have known theoretical solutions verified by the photoelastic and other methods (compression and extension of specimens, pressure of a concentrated force and a sphere on an elastic semi-infinite solid, and so forth) and some have no theoretical solution at all (for example the deformations under arbitrarily applied loads, the measurement of strain in the elastic-plastic region of the material, and others).

The results of experimental work on stresses and strains in linear, plane and three-dimensional states of stress under static load conditions are given in this Chapter.

17. THE MEASURING EQUIPMENT USED IN THE EXPERIMENTS

In the examples of experimental solutions that follow, equipment suitable for static and dynamic measurements was used. For time-variable strains (including those which vary slowly) a four-channel electronic amplifier type TU–4M was employed.

The measuring bridge is fed with a voltage of $5-7$ V at a frequency of the order of 6000 c/s; the voltage taken from the output terminals of the bridge is amplified and rectified; the carrier frequency is filtered out and the signal then transmitted to the galvo coil of a mirror oscillograph. The unbalance of the bridge, which occurs when mechanical stresses of $400-500$ kg/cm^2 ($5700-7100$ lb/in^2) are measured in steel with 0.03 mm constantan strain gauges having a base length of 20 mm and a resistance of 200 Ω, produces an electric voltage signal which, if supplied to the input of the amplifier, gives a current of 20 mA through the output terminals of the amplifier into the vibrating coil. The basic circuit of the amplifier channel is given in Fig. 31. The voltage is fed from the output terminals of the bridge to the amplifier input. The input 1 to the amplifier is symmetrical, so that the arms of the bridge can be balanced up to the extent of 1 Ω when they become unbalanced. The resistive components of the bridge are balanced with the aid of a potentiometer 2, the reactive components with a potentiometer connected to the central point of the bridge. Moving the slider to one side or the other reduces the resistance of one arm, while increasing the resistance of the other.

The signal from the output terminals of the bridge travels through a step-up transformer 3 and a stepped potentiometer 4 to the control grid of the first amplifier stage, which consists of a 6J4 pentode 5 provided with negative current feedback. The output from the pentode is coupled through a capacitance 6 and a stepless gain control 7 to the second amplifier stage 8 (pentode 6J4), which is the same as the first stage except for the provision of voltage feedback.

The anode voltages of the first two stages of the master oscillator 9 and the screen grids of the valves of the output and buffer stages are stabilized by an electronic stabilising tube.

Bridge balancing is monitored by a magic eye 6E5 indicator 10 connected to the anode circuit of the second stage.

The output stage consists of a 6F6 pentode 11 with negative current feedback.

A phase-sensitive bridge 12 is employed as a rectifying device; it consists of four selenium rectifiers in series with resistances connected in a bridge circuit. The control voltage from the buffer stage (6F6 pentode) 13 is injected into one pair of terminals of the phase-sensitive bridge 12 through a transformer; the other pair of terminals receives the investigated voltage from the output stage of the amplifier. The buffer-stage transformer

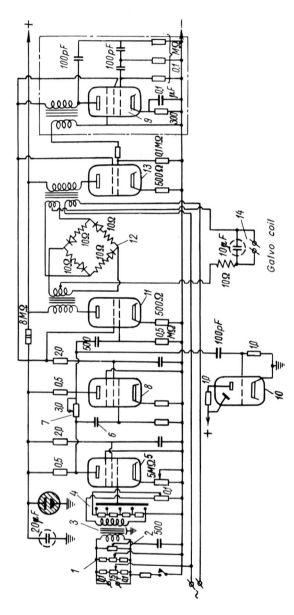

Fig. 31. Basic circuit of one channel of the TU–4M strain measuring device

also provides the voltage supply for the measuring bridge formed by the strain gauges.

From the output of the phase-sensitive rectifier bridge the signal is passed through a filter circuit to the vibrating galvo coils 14.

The master oscillator, a 6J4 pentode 9, is common to all four channels of the installation; it supplies voltages with a carrier

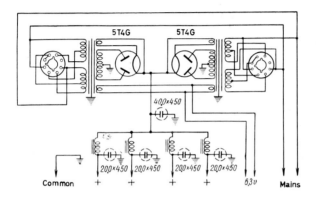

FIG. 32. Rectifier circuit for the strain
measuring device

frequency of the order of 6000 c/s to the grids of all the buffer stages.

The oscillator is provided with a stabilized anode voltage. The rectifier uses type 5T4 G valves and is arranged in a full-wave circuit (Fig. 32).

For static measurements the authors have used equipment developed at the Scientific Research Institute for Bridges, which is attached to the Leningrad Railway Transport Research Institute [43].

The electric circuit (Fig. 33) is based on a balanced d.c. resistance bridge using the null method of reading. The two arms of the bridge containing the active gauge (R_a) and the compensating gauge (R_k) are brought outside the instrument, the other two resistance arms $(R_1$ and $R_2)$ are placed inside. A number of resistances R_d enabling the bridge to be balanced in stages of 200 scale units each, are connected in series with the internal arms. Accurate balancing is provided by a measuring slide-wire R_p with a resistance equal to one resistance stage of R_d. The measuring slide-wire is shunted by a variable resistance R_{sc} acting as a sensitivity control; it permits the sensitivity of the circuit to be changed or selected in such a way that the scale divisions of the instruments can be kept in units of strain when working with strain gauges of different gauge factors.

The magnitude of the supply current is controlled by a rheostat R_n and monitored on a milliammeter mA.

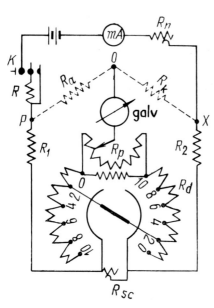

FIG. 33. Bridge circuit for measuring static strains

The indicating instrument may be any galvanometer with a scale reading from 1×10^{-7} to 4×10^{-8} A/div. A strain gauge selector switch is used in combination with this instrument.

18. MEASUREMENT OF STRESSES INSIDE COMPONENTS IN A LINEAR STATE OF STRESS

Most problems with a linear state of stress can be solved theoretically so that the linear state of stress offers a comparatively simple check on the reliability of the experimental method. For this reason a few data are given here about stresses in compression, tension and bending measured with the aid of special unbonded wire strain gauges.

Pure tension and compression

As has been stated already, the main requirements for strain gauges to be used in strain measurements are that the gauge grid should faithfully follow the strains of the component to which it is cemented, and that the relationship between its change in resistance and the magnitude of the strain should be

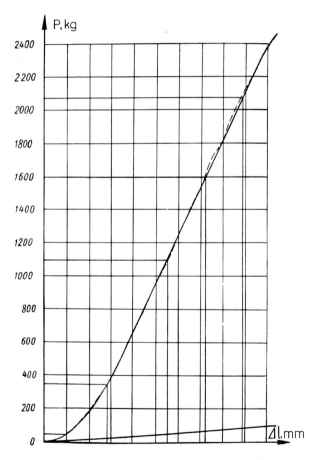

FIG. 34. Load-compression diagrams plotted from autographic and oscillographic records

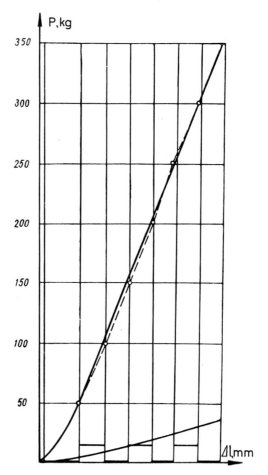

FIG. 35. Load-extension diagrams plotted from autographic and oscillographic records

linear. Provided these conditions are fulfilled, an unbonded wire strain gauge placed inside a model or specimen can be used for measuring the strains at internal points of models or members.

As a check of these main conditions, tension and compression tests of specimens with embedded unbonded wire gauges on a

Gagarin or IM–4R testing machine with simultaneous recording on an MPO–2 mirror oscillograph showed that there is indeed a linear relationship between strains and stresses on both the autographic record and the oscillograms.

Figure 34 gives the load-deflection curve of a specimen compressed in a Gagarin testing machine and, underneath, an oscillogram of the strains in a gauge placed inside the specimen. The dotted curve of Fig. 34 has been derived from the oscillogram data with an enlarged vertical scale. It is evident from these curves that the autographic and the oscillograph records coincide.

A similar relationship between load and deflexion (strain) is obtained when the specimens are in tension. Figure 35 gives the load-extension curve of a specimen tested on an IM–4R press (full line) and the curve plotted from the oscillogram (dotted line). The oscillogram is shown at the bottom of Fig. 35.

Under repeated static loading in both compression and tension within the elastic limits of the specimen, the results of the measurements with the embedded gauges remained the same.

In addition, tests were carried out with embedded gauges and gauges cemented to the surface. Both types of gauges reflected the linear character of the dependence between strains and stresses.

Comparative tests on specimens with and without strain gauges showed that the installation of unbonded short base-length gauges inside the specimens does not alter their elastic properties or strength.

Thus, the investigation of the linear state of stress of specimens made from epoxy resin has established that in the elastic range the wire strain gauges introduced into the specimens reflect without any distortion the character of the relationship between the strains and the loads applied.

Pure bending

Figure 36 (a) shows the loading diagram of a beam subjected to pure bending. The greatest bending moment occurs over the length AB and is

$$M = P \cdot a.$$

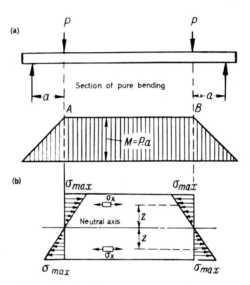

FIG. 36. Loading, moment and stress diagrams for a beam in pure bending

The stresses in pure bending are determined by

$$\sigma_x = \frac{M \cdot z}{J}, \qquad \sigma_z = 0, \qquad \tau_{xz} = 0,$$

where M is the bending moment, J the second moment of area about the neutral axis and z the distance from the neutral axis to the point investigated.

The longitudinal stresses σ_x in the extended or compressed zone of the length AB of the beam remain constant along lines equidistant from the neutral axis [Fig. 36 (b)]. Hence, wire strain gauges placed inside the beam at points equidistant from the neutral axis within the portion under pure bending should give identical readings under load.

For an experimental confirmation that the strain gauges work correctly under conditions of pure bending, a small beam 150 mm long, 30 mm deep and 15 mm wide was prepared from epoxy resin; strain gauges with a base length of 2 mm were embedded in this beam in the positions shown in Fig. 37. The gauges 1 to 5 in the compressed zone and 1′ to 5′ in the extended zone of the beam were at a distance of 10 mm from the neutral axis.

The beam was tested on a UP–6 machine (Fig. 39); the resistance of the gauges under load was measured with a static strain measuring equipment by the null method (see Section 17). The instrument had a sensitivity adjustable between 1×10^{-3} and 1×10^{-5} strain per unit scale reading. The value of one scale division in terms of the stresses was established by calibration of a cylindrical specimen and found to be 0.5 kg/cm^2 (7 lb/in^2).

The results of the measurements with the beam statically loaded by forces from 5 to 25 kg are given in Table 9.

TABLE 9.

Load (kg)	Compressed zone					Extended zone				
	No. of strain gauge (from Fig. 37)									
	1	*2*	*3*	*4*	*5*	*1′*	*2′*	*3′*	*4′*	*5′*
5	5.5 / 2.75	5.5 / 2.75	5.5 / 2.75	5.5 / 2.75	5.5 / 2.75	5.5 / 2.5	5.5 / 2.75	6 / 3	5.5 / 2.75	5.5 / 2.75
10	11 / 5.5	11 / 5.5	11 / 5.5	11 / 5.5	11 / 5.5	11 / 5.5	11 / 5.5	12 / 6	11 / 5.5	11 / 5.5
15	17 / 8.5	17 / 8.5	17 / 8.5	17 / 8.5	17 / 8.5	17 / 8.5	17 / 8.5	18 / 9	17 / 8.5	17 / 8.5
20	23 / 11.5	23 / 11.5	23 / 11.5	23 / 11.5	23 / 11.5	23 / 11.5	23 / 11.5	24 / 12	23 / 11.5	23 / 11.5
25	29 / 14.5	29 / 14.5	29 / 14.5	29 / 14.5	29 / 14.5	29 / 14.5	29 / 14.5	30 / 15	29 / 14.5	29 / 14.5

Note: The numerators give the instrument readings, the denominators the magnitude of the stresses in kg/cm^2

As a comparison with the experimental results, the stresses were calculated theoretically for the points where the gauges were mounted. The design diagrams for the beam are given in Fig. 36; the data for the calculation are as follows: the load P varies from 5–25 kg, the distance from the neutral axis to the

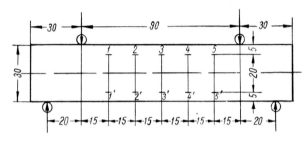

FIG. 37. Diagram of wire strain gauge positions
inside a beam in pure bending

position of the gauges is $z = \pm 10$ mm, the width of the beam 15 mm, its height 30 mm, the distance between support and load (the arm of the force couple) $a = 20$ mm. The results of the calculation are given in Table 10.

TABLE 10.

Load (kg)	Stress in kg/cm²
5	$\pm\ 2.96$
10	$\pm\ 5.92$
15	$\pm\ 8.88$
20	± 11.84
25	± 14.80

Tables 9 and 10 prove that the results obtained theoretically and experimentally are in satisfactory agreement.

The phenomenon of pure bending is extremely simple from the theoretical point of view, but in practice it is quite difficult to obtain the correct value of the stresses for a specified value of the bending moment because of certain difficulties connected with the loading of the model. In the example described the load on the beam was transmitted through rolls; hence at the points of application of the load (as well as at the supports) there were undoubtedly friction forces F_1 and F_2 (Fig. 38), and these usually reduce the bending moment and cause displacements on the

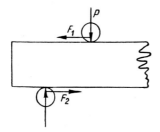

FIG. 38. Diagram of
friction forces

neutral axis of the beam. This reduction in the bending moment due to the friction forces will lower the experimental results (but only slightly).

These examples show that the calibration of embedded wire strain gauges in simple tension or compression gives more reliable results than are obtained in pure bending. The results found in pure bending will be slightly lower unless special measures are taken to reduce the influence of the friction forces at the points of load application and at the supports of the beam under test.

19. AN EXAMPLE FOR THE MEASUREMENT OF STRESSES INSIDE COMPONENTS IN A PLANE STATE OF STRESS

The results obtained from testing specimens with unbonded wire strain gauges in tension, compression and bending allow us to proceed to the solution of more complex problems, in particular problems relating to the stress distribution in local stress concentrations of various members.

The example chosen here is the measurement of the stress concentration in a plate with a central circular hole under uniaxial static tension. A general view of the testing arrangement is shown in Fig. 39.

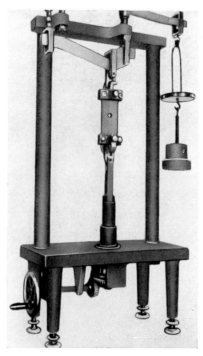

FIG. 39. Tensile test of a plate
with a central circular hole

Ten unbonded strain gauges (points 1 to 5 and $1'$ to $5'$ in Fig. 40) were located in the cross-section coinciding with the transverse axis of the hole. The direction of the gauges coincided with the direction of the principal stresses σ_x and σ_y. The gauge positions and the dimensions of the plate can be seen in Fig. 40.

The stress distribution and the magnitude of the concentrated stresses were determined for two different sizes of the central hole. A hole of 10 mm dia. was drilled first. After the stresses had been determined and recorded on the film of an MPO–2 mirror oscillograph, the hole dia. was increased to 16 mm. The gauges 2 and 2' (Fig. 40) then occupied positions corresponding to those

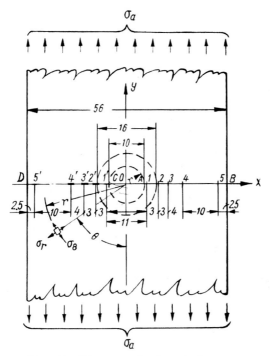

FIG. 40. Diagram of wire strain-gauge positions in a plate with a circular hole:

1–5: positions of strain gauges parallel to axis OY;
1'–5': positions of strain gauges parallel to axis OX

previously held by the gauges 1 and 1'; this was achieved by suitable positioning of the gauges when mounted in the mould of the plate.

With both holes the measurements were taken at three stages of loading; 50, 100 and 150 kg. Tables 11 and 12 present the data obtained experimentally for σ_x and σ_y under a load of 150 kg.

In a plate, the unbonded strain gauges can be calibrated without preparation of special calibrating specimens.

6

TABLE 11.

Load (kg)	Hole dia. (mm)	Stresses σ_y from strain-gauge readings in kg/cm² (Fig. 40)				
		1	2	3	4	5
150	10	130.5	70.47	60.03	57.42	54.81
	16	—	140.94	86.13	66.81	56.37

TABLE 12.

Load (kg)	Hole dia. (mm)	Stresses σ_x from strain-gauge readings in kg/cm² (Fig. 40)				
		1′	2′	3′	4′	5′
150	10	10.44	18.27	12.52	7.83	2.61
	16	—	7.83	20.88	15.66	5.22

The plate was here subjected to tension in a testing machine after it had been machined to the finished dimensions but before the drilling of the central hole. From the known values of the loads, the dimensions of the plate and the stress readings on the recording instrument (the amplitude of the MPO–2 oscillograph record), the calibration data for the active gauges in the plate could be determined. The value of one division (one millimeter deflection on the oscillograph film) was found to be 5.22 kg/cm² (74.3 lb/in²) for the gauges in the plate.

The theoretical stresses for plates of this type in uniaxial tension can be computed from the following formulae:

$$\sigma_r = \frac{\sigma_a}{2}\left[\left(1 - \frac{r_0^2}{r^2}\right) + \left(1 - \frac{4r_0^2}{r^2} + \frac{3r_0^4}{r^4}\right)\cos 2\Theta\right],$$

$$\sigma_\theta = \frac{\sigma_a}{2}\left[\left(1 + \frac{r_0^2}{r^2}\right) - \left(1 + \frac{3r_0^4}{r^4}\right)\cos 2\Theta\right].$$

Taking $\Theta = \pi/2$ (Fig. 40), we obtain an expression for the stresses σ_x and σ_y acting in the cross-section of the OX-axis:

$$\sigma_{r_{\theta = 90}} = \frac{3}{2}\,\sigma_a\left(\frac{r_0^2}{x^2} - \frac{r_0^4}{x^4}\right),$$

$$\sigma_{\theta_{\theta = 90}} = \frac{\sigma_a}{2}\left(2 + \frac{r_0^2}{x^2} + \frac{3r_0^4}{x^4}\right),$$

or

$$\sigma_x = \frac{3}{2}\,\sigma_a\left(\frac{d^2}{4x^2} - \frac{d^4}{16x^4}\right),$$

$$\sigma_y = \frac{\sigma_a}{2}\left(2 + \frac{d^2}{4x^2} + \frac{3d^4}{16x^4}\right),$$

where $d = 2r_0$ is the diameter of the hole.

The calculated stresses for the points of the gauges 1–5 and $1'$–$5'$ and for the points A, B and C, D on the boundaries (as indicated in Fig. 40) are given in Tables 13 and 14.

TABLE 13.

Load (kg)	Hole dia. (mm)	Stresses σ_y in kg/cm² at points:						
		A	1	2	3	4	5	B
150	10	160.68	130.60	72.44	61.49	57.21	54.69	54.42
	16	—	160.68	140.18	85.26	66.36	56.67	56.27

TABLE 14

Load (kg)	Hole dia. (mm)	Stresses σ_x in kg/cm² at the points:						
		C	1'	2'	3'	4'	5'	D
150	10	0	11.49	18.18	12.29	7.55	2.90	0
	16	—	0	8.19	20.87	15.74	7.1	0

Figure 41 shows the stresses σ_x and σ_y obtained from theory and experiment. The agreement of the results is evident.

The experimental investigation of the stress distribution and the magnitude of the stresses in a plate with a central circular

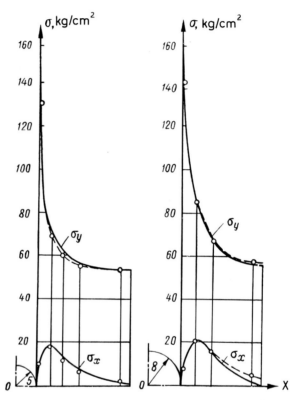

FIG. 41. Diagrams of the stresses σ_y and σ_x in a plate with a central hole:

——— values obtained theoretically;
- - - - - - - values obtained experimentally

hole under uniaxial static tension thus demonstrates that strain measurement by embedded electric-resistance gauges can be used to solve a wide variety of problems connected with the study of stress concentrations in plane components of machines and mechanisms.

20. EXAMPLES FOR THE MEASUREMENT
OF STRESSES INSIDE COMPONENTS
IN A THREE-DIMENSIONAL STATE OF STRESS

The problem of ensuring the strength of components in a three-dimensional state of stress is gaining in importance every day. The increase in the load capacity and speed of machines with a simultaneous reduction in their weight means that at the present time the service life and the conditions for the safety of members and components are determined by contact stresses (bearings, races, wheels of rolling stock, rails and so forth).

Up to the present many contact problems in mechanical engineering have not been solved theoretically. For example, the pressure distribution in ball races is not yet known, not to mention the solution of more complex problems. Experimental studies of three-dimensional problems are therefore of great interest for design and research work.

In this section a few examples of experimental solutions for three-dimensional problems under static loading are described.

Compression of crossed cylinders

Below are given the experimental and theoretical solutions to one of the problems in computing the greatest stresses when two circular cylinders with mutually perpendicular axes are pressed against each other. The radius of the first cylinder is 250 mm, that of the second 300 mm.

Unbonded wire strain gauges were mounted in the mould for the smaller cylinder in positions selected also for the theoretical evaluation. The magnitude and distribution of the stresses σ_z, σ_x and σ_y (the normal stresses along the three axes) at points on the line of symmetry through the centre of the surface of contact of the two cylinders, i.e. on the Z-axis (Fig. 42), were determined experimentally and theoretically as a function of the depth below the surface of the points investigated.

It has been stated in Section 14 that the system of locating the strain gauges depends upon the shape of the component. In fairly long components with a constant cross-section (beams, cylinders, columns, rolled profiles, etc.) it is technically most expedient not to mount the gauges in the form of multi-component rosettes, but as individual groups of single gauges. The

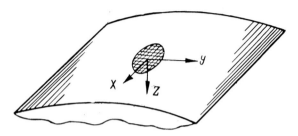

FIG. 42. Surface of contact of two crossed cylinders

shape of the cylinders permits the use of this method of locating the gauges (Fig. 43).

The unbonded strain gauges at points 2–9 (Fig. 43) were prepared in the form of two-component rosettes orientated along

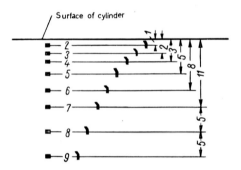

FIG. 43. Diagram of wire strain gauge positions in test cylinder:
— wire strain gauges orientated along x-axis;
Ʌ two-component rosettes with gauges orientated along z- and y-axes

the z- and y-axes (Fig. 42). At another section, single gauges orientated along the x-axis were placed at the same distances from the surface of the cylinder. In all, 24 single unbonded strain-gauge grids were embedded in the cylinder.

The selected method of locating the gauges slightly increases the amount of work involved in the strain measurements, because the relative position of the cylinders has to be changed for measurements with each individual gauge. In the case of multi-component strain-gauge rosettes all the gauges comprising one rosette could have been measured in one testing position.

In the present example, the loading device pressing the two cylinders against each other was provided with a stage containing a coordinate adjusting attachment. The model cylinder with the embedded gauges was fixed to this stage in the correct orientation. The other cylinder—the die cylinder—was fixed to the upper support of the loading device with its axis set perpendicular to the generators of the lower model cylinder. The cylinder under test was moved successively into the position of each cross-section in which a strain gauge was located. The work was carried out with the static strain-measuring equipment.

Table 15 lists the scale readings of the instrument and the strains in the direction of the z-, x- and y-axes under a load of 300 kg, which was also used as a basis for plotting the experimental strain curves ε_z', ε_x' and ε_y' (Fig. 47) for the model cylinder. The value of one scale division C of the instrument, obtained by calibration specimens, is 1.512×10^{-5} strain units.

TABLE 15.

Point	z (mm)	Instrument reading	$\varepsilon_z' \times 10^5$	Instrument reading	$\varepsilon_x' \times 10^5$	Instrument reading	$\varepsilon_y' \times 10^5$
3	2	−385	−582.12	+ 48	+ 72.57	+ 57	+ 86.18
4	3	−390	−589.68	+ 80	+120.96	+ 92	+139.10
5	5	−345	−521.64	+100	+151.20	+108	+163.29
6	8	−240	−362.88	+ 75	+113.40	+ 85	+128.52
7	11	−175	−264.60	+ 60	+ 90.72	+ 62	+ 93.74
8	16	− 93	−140.61	+ 35	+ 52.92	+ 30	+ 45.36
9	21	− 60	− 90.72	+ 25	+ 37.8	+ 20	+ 30.24

Note: Value of one division $C = 1.512 \times 10^{-5}$ strain; ε' denotes experimental strain values

The magnitude of the stresses at the gauge points is found
from Hooke's law which gives the stresses when the strains are
known

$$\sigma_z = \lambda\,\Theta + 2G\,\varepsilon_z,$$
$$\sigma_x = \lambda\,\Theta + 2G\,\varepsilon_x,$$
$$\sigma_y = \lambda\,\Theta + 2G\,\varepsilon_y,$$

with the volume strain

$$\Theta = \varepsilon_z + \varepsilon_x + \varepsilon_y,$$

the modulus of rigidity

$$G = \frac{E}{2\,(1+\mu)},$$

and

$$\lambda = \frac{E\mu}{(1+\mu)\,(1-2\mu)},$$

where $E = 3.5 \times 10^4\,\text{kg/cm}^2$ (498,000 lb/in^2) is Young's modulus,
and $\mu = 0.36$ is Poisson's ratio.

The stresses σ_z', σ_x' and σ_y' computed from the experimental
strains are given in Table 16.

TABLE 16.

Point	z (mm)	$\lambda\,\Theta$	$2G\,\varepsilon_z'$	$2G\,\varepsilon_x'$	$2G\,\varepsilon_y'$	σ_z' kg/cm^2	σ_x' kg/cm^2	σ_y' kg/cm^2
3	2	−140.08	−149.81	+18.67	+22.17	−289.89	−121.41	−117.91
4	3	−109.06	−151.75	+31.13	+35.79	−260.81	− 77.93	− 73.27
5	5	− 68.54	−134.24	+38.91	+42.02	−202.78	−29.63	− 26.52
6	8	− 40.02	− 93.38	+29.18	+33.07	−133.40	−10.84	− 6.95
7	11	− 26.51	− 68.09	+23.34	+24.12	− 94.60	− 3.17	− 2.39
8	16	− 14.00	− 36.18	+13.61	+11.67	− 50.18	− 0.39	− 2.33
9	21	− 7.50	− 23.34	+ 9.72	+ 7.78	− 30.84	− 2.22	+ 0.28

This investigation provided an opportunity to determine not
only the maximum strains ε_z', which are measured when the
strain gauges are located on the line of symmetry underneath the

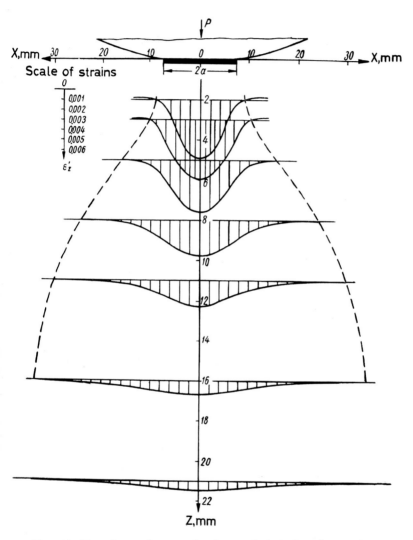

FIG. 44. Experimental curves for the vertical strains ε_z' at various depths z; $2a = 15$ mm is the experimental value of the major axis of the contact ellipse

centre of the surface of contact, but also the strains in gauges located in off-centre positions.

Figure 44 shows experimental curves for the vertical strain distribution at various depths underneath the contact region (with different gauge positions) outside the line of symmetry through the centre of contact. From these curves it is evident that the area over which the vertical strains are distributed depends

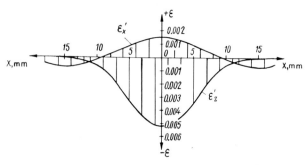

Fig. 45. Experimental curves for the strains ε'_z and ε'_x at a point 5 mm below the surface of contact

upon the depth of the layer investigated. The area is smaller for the upper horizontal layers and larger for the lower layers.

The boundaries of these areas (they have been obtained for the other two coordinate directions as well) can be used to estimate the deformed region of the contacting bodies in compression.

Figure 45 gives the experimental curves for the axial distribution of the vertical (ε'_z) and the longitudinal horizontal (ε'_x) strains at point 5, which is 5 mm below the surface of the contact area. The curves show that the strains in the direction of the x-axis change sign at a certain distance from the contact area. This indicates that when a cylinder rolls under load, the strains in the direction of the x-axis are alternating in character.

The theoretical calculation for the stresses in the cylinder at the gauge positions is carried out by methods developed on the basis of the Hertz–Dinnik–Belyayev theory, which consists of the following: If it is assumed that the contact area is small in comparison with the size of the cylinders and located at a fair distance from their ends, then the contact stresses and the stresses on the line of symmetry through the centre of the contact area can be calculated from the theory of elasticity.

For the stresses at points on the line of symmetry through the centre of the contact area of the cylinders, the following formulae have been suggested by Professor Belyayev [7, 8]:

$$\sigma_z = - q_0 \beta \frac{\sin^2 \varphi}{\sqrt{1 - e^2 \sin^2 \varphi}},$$

$$\sigma_x = - q_0 \beta \left[- \frac{\lambda + 2G}{\lambda + G} \cdot \frac{z}{a} \cdot \frac{1}{e^2} (F - E) + \right.$$
$$+ \frac{\lambda}{\lambda + G} \cdot \frac{1}{\beta^2} \left(\sqrt{1 - e^2 \sin^2 \varphi} - \frac{z}{a} E \right) +$$
$$\left. + \frac{G}{\lambda + G} \cdot \frac{1}{e^2} (1 - \sqrt{1 - e^2 \sin^2 \varphi}) \right],$$

$$\sigma_y = - q_0 \beta \left[\frac{\lambda + 2G}{\lambda + G} \cdot \frac{z}{a} \cdot \frac{1}{e^2} (F - E) + \right.$$
$$+ \frac{\lambda + 2G}{\lambda + G} \frac{1}{\beta^2} \cdot \left(\frac{\cos^2 \varphi}{\sqrt{1 - e^2 \sin^2 \varphi}} \right) + \frac{\lambda}{\lambda + G} \cdot \frac{1}{\beta^2} \sqrt{1 - e^2 \sin^2 \varphi} \frac{2}{\beta^2} \cdot \frac{z}{a} E +$$
$$\left. + \frac{G}{\lambda + G} \cdot \frac{1}{e^2} \left(\frac{1}{\sqrt{1 - e^2 \sin^2 \varphi}} - 1 \right) \right].$$

In these formulae:

$q_0 = \dfrac{3P}{2\pi a b}$ is the normal stress at the centre of the contact plane;

P is the force compressing the contacting bodies;

a is the major semi-axis of the contact ellipse;

b is the minor semi-axis of the contact ellipse;

$\beta = \dfrac{b}{a}$ is the ratio of the semi-axes;

$e = \sqrt{1 - \beta^2}$ is the eccentricity of the contact ellipse;

z is the distance of the point on the z-axis from the contact area;

$\varphi = \cot^{-1} z/a$;

$F(e, \varphi)$ is the elliptic integral of the first kind with the modulus e and the upper limit φ;

$E(e, \varphi)$ is the elliptic integral of the second kind;

λ and G are determined from the formulae given earlier;

σ_z, σ_x and σ_y are the principal stresses at the given point.

The magnitudes of the semi-axes of the contact area are determined on the basis of the following considerations.

When the force compressing the cylinders approaches zero, contact occurs at a single point. With increasing force the cylinders begin to make contact over an increasing area bounded by a closed contour.

The undeformed surfaces of the two contacting bodies in the vicinity of their point of contact can be represented approximately by second-order surfaces. The initial distance $z_1 + z_2$ between two points, one on each cylinder, that will be brought to coincidence inside the surface of contact by the applied compressive force can then be written

$$z_1 + z_2 = Ax^2 + By^2,$$

where x, y are the coordinate axes perpendicular to the common normal at the point of contact; and A, B are constant coefficients depending on the magnitudes of the principal curvatures of the contacting surfaces and on the angle between the planes of principal curvature of the two surfaces [37]:

$$A + B = \frac{1}{2}\left(\frac{1}{R_1} + \frac{1}{R_1'} + \frac{1}{R_2} + \frac{1}{R_2'}\right),$$

$$B - A = \frac{1}{2}\left[\left(\frac{1}{R_1} - \frac{1}{R_1'}\right)^2 + \left(\frac{1}{R_2} - \frac{1}{R_2'}\right)^2 + \right.$$
$$\left. + 2\left(\frac{1}{R_1} - \frac{1}{R_1'}\right)\left(\frac{1}{R_2} - \frac{1}{R_2'}\right)\cos 2\psi\right]^{1/2}.$$

Here R_1 and R_1' denote the principal radii of curvature of one solid at the point of contact, R_2 and R_2' those of the other solid, ψ the angle between the principal planes containing the radii R_1 and R_2.

For two contacting circular cylinders with $\psi = 90°$,

$$A + B = \frac{1}{2}\left(\frac{1}{R_1} + \frac{1}{R_2}\right),$$

$$B - A = \frac{1}{2}\left(\frac{1}{R_2} - \frac{1}{R_1}\right),$$

or

$$A = \frac{1}{2 R_1} \text{ and } B = \frac{1}{2 R_2},$$

where R_1 is the radius of the large cylinder and R_2 the radius of the smaller cylinder.

When the two cylinders approach each other, the coordinates of points on the boundary of the surface of contact satisfy the following equation, as shown by Professor Belyayev [38]:

$$\frac{x^2}{2 R_1} + \frac{y^2}{2 R_2} = \alpha = \text{const.}$$

This is the equation of an ellipse with semi-axes in the directions of the coordinate axes, the major semi-axis coinciding with the x-axis, i.e. parallel with the generators of the small cylinder, and the minor semi-axis b coinciding with the y-axis, i.e. parallel with the generators of the larger cylinder. The magnitudes of the semi-axes of the contact ellipse for contacting bodies of the assumed shape are determined by the formulae:

$$a = m \sqrt[3]{\frac{3\pi P (K_1 + K_2)}{4 (A + B)}},$$

$$b = n \sqrt[3]{\frac{3\pi P (K_1 + K_2)}{4 (A + B)}},$$

where m and n are coefficients depending on the ratio

$$\frac{B - A}{A + B} = \cos \Theta$$

and have been tabulated as functions of the angle Θ by Timo-shenko [37],

$$K_1 = \frac{1 - \mu_1^2}{\pi\,E_1} \text{ and } K_2 = \frac{1 - \mu_2^2}{\pi\,E_2}$$

with μ_1, μ_2 as Poisson's ratios and E_1, E_2 as Young's moduli of elasticity of the two bodies in contact.

Since in the tests the same material was used for both cylinders,

$$K_1 = K_2 \text{ and } (K_1 + K_2) = 2K.$$

The magnitudes of the semi-axes of the contact ellipse computed theoretically for a force $P = 300$ kg (the force taken in the experiments) are: $a = 0.72$ cm and $b = 0.635$ cm.

The magnitudes of the semi-axes of the contact ellipse determined experimentally on the basis of impressions made with cigarette and carbon paper are: $a = 0.75$ cm, $b = 0.65$ cm.

The slightly higher experimental data can be explained by the deformation and creasing of the cigarette and carbon papers at the boundaries of the surface of contact.

The given formulae were used to compute the stresses σ_z, σ_x and σ_y for points located at different depths on the z-axis passing through the centre of contact. The results are given in Table 17 and Fig. 46.

TABLE 17.

Point	z mm	σ_z kg/cm²	σ_x kg/cm²	σ_y kg/cm²
1	0	−313.49	−267.06	−272.59
2	1	−306.78	−183.74	−183.04
3	2	−288.23	−122.42	−118.76
4	3	−261.84	− 79.74	− 75.24
5	5	−202.66	− 32.46	− 29.04
6	8	−130.75	− 7.87	− 6.57
7	11	− 86.13	− 1.32	− 1.08
8	16	− 47.63	+ 0.73	+ 0.58
9	21	− 29.56	+ 0.89	+ 0.79

Since strains were measured in the experiments, the magnitudes of the strains were also calculated theoretically for a comparison of theoretical and experimental results.

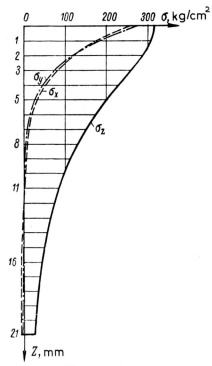

FIG. 46. Theoretical curves for the stresses σ_z, σ_x, σ_y

It is well known from the theory of elasticity that in a three-dimensional state of stress with the stresses σ_z, σ_x and σ_y the strains are defined by

$$\varepsilon_z = \frac{1}{E}\left[\sigma_z - \mu\left(\sigma_x + \sigma_y\right)\right],$$

$$\varepsilon_x = \frac{1}{E}\left[\sigma_x - \mu\left(\sigma_y + \sigma_z\right)\right],$$

$$\varepsilon_y = \frac{1}{E}\left[\sigma_y - \mu\left(\sigma_x + \sigma_z\right)\right].$$

The strains calculated with these formulae from the theoretical stress values (Table 17) are given in Table 18.

TABLE 18.

Point	z (mm)	$\varepsilon_z \times 10^5$	$\varepsilon_x \times 10^5$	$\varepsilon_y \times 10^5$
1	0	− 340.63	−160.19	−181.71
2	1	−499.26	− 21.17	− 18.46
3	2	−575.46	+ 68.86	+ 84.08
4	3	−588.71	+118.88	+136.37
5	5	−515.77	+145.57	+158.86
6	8	−358.74	+118.77	+123.79
7	11	−243.63	+ 85.91	+ 86.86
8	16	−137.43	+ 60.45	+ 49.88
9	21	− 86.17	+ 32.14	+ 31.74

Figure 47 gives both the theoretical and the experimental strain curves. It can be seen from these curves that the experimental strains ε_x' are slightly lower than the theoretical strains, whereas ε_z' and ε_y' are slightly higher than the theoretical values (within the limits of 1–4%). From a comparison of the data one can draw the conclusion that the results agree satisfactorily and that this agreement is within the limits of accuracy for the calculations.

Since the directions of the principal planes and the magnitudes of the principal stresses acting on these planes are known, the values of the maximum shear stresses τ_{max} acting in planes at 45° to the principal planes are

$$\tau_{max} = \frac{\sigma_{max} - \sigma_{min}}{2}.$$

It can be seen from the maximum shear stress curves (Fig. 48) that the stress differences decay much more slowly than the principal stresses.

Professor Belyayev [8] has stated that it is not the principal stresses but the differences between the principal stresses which determine the strength of a material, and that from this point of view the state of stress at points on the z-axis is equivalent to simple tension with a maximum normal stress equal to $\sigma_z - \sigma_y$. Therefore, the maximum shear stress occurs in planes parallel to the x-axis and to the bisector of the angle between the y- and

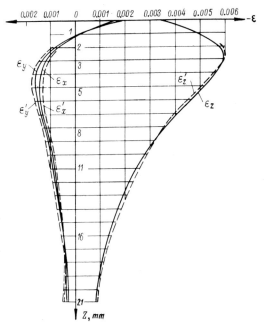

FIG. 47. Theoretical and experimental
curves for the strains:
———— theoretical; - - - - - - experimental

z-axes. The region of maximum shear stress, as can be seen from Fig. 48, is located at a small distance below the surface of the cylinder.

It has been established by the experiments described here that the strains in the direction of the x- and y-axes change their signs (Fig. 45). The magnitude of the strain—positive or negative—depends first upon the depth of the point examined, secondly upon its distance (along the x-axis) from the centre of contact.

7

The experiments have also shown that the amplitudes of the alternating strain ε_x (Fig. 45) are comparatively small near the surface of contact, increase to a maximum at a certain depth (4—6 mm from the surface, in the region of the maximum shearing

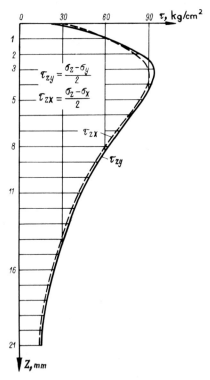

FIG. 48. Theoretical curves for the maximum shearing stresses

stresses) and then again decrease. This gives grounds for the assumption that deep fractures under conditions of pure rolling without tangential loads may be caused by an alternating cycle of strains which have their greatest values in the region of the maximum shearing stresses.

Pressure of a circular die on an elastic half-space
(Shtayerman's problem)

For an experimental analysis of the strain distribution when a circular cylindrical die presses on an elastic half-space, a model of the half-space was prepared in the form of a cylinder with embedded unbonded wire strain gauges. These gauges were located at points of certain horizontal sections of the cylinder as shown diagrammatically in Fig. 49. They were orientated along the z-, x- and y-axes.

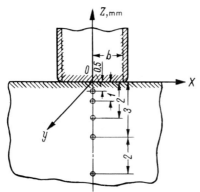

FIG. 49. Cylindrical die pressing
on an elastic half-space
o = positions of strain gauges

The load was applied to the upper surface of the model cylinder through a cylindrical steel die.

Shtayerman [39] has stated that if b denotes the radius of the circle of initial contact between die and elastic half-space, then the radius a of the contact region under compression is slightly greater than its initial value b.

If the shape of the die (the diameter of its base and the curvature of its edges), the elastic constants of die and half-space and the compressive force P are known, the pressure distribution over the area of contact can be determined by the formula [39]:

$$q_0(r) = \frac{3 \cos^2 \varphi}{3 \sin \varphi + \sin^3 \varphi_0 - 3\varphi_0 \cos \varphi_0} \, \psi\left(\frac{r}{b}\right) \frac{P}{\pi\, b^2}, \quad 0 < r < a,$$

7*

where φ_0 is $\cos^{-1} \dfrac{b}{a}$,

  b is the radius of the circle of initial contact,
  a is the radius of the circle of contact under the load P,
  P is the compressive load,

$$\psi(x) = \int_0^{\varphi_0} \frac{(2 \tan \varphi - \varphi) \tan \varphi \, d\varphi}{\sqrt{1 - x^2 \cos^2 \varphi}} \qquad \text{when } 0 < x < 1,$$

$$\psi(x) = \int_{\cos^{-1} \frac{1}{x}}^{\varphi_0} \frac{(2 \tan \varphi - \varphi) \tan \varphi \, d\varphi}{\sqrt{1 - x^2 \cos^2 \varphi}} \qquad \text{when } 1 < x < \frac{1}{\cos \varphi}.$$

These formulae were used as the basis for the theoretical determination of the pressure distribution over the area of con-

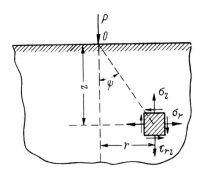

FIG. 50. Concentrated force
acting on an elastic half-space

tact under the die. The pressure in turn represented the load assumed in the subsequent theoretical calculations for the stresses inside the elastic half-space. The form of the distributed load is shown in Fig. 51.

Since the intensity of the load on the surface of the elastic half-space is difficult to express as a functional relation, the magnitudes of the stresses at points located in various sections and at various depths are determined in the following manner. The distributed load shown in Fig. 51 is replaced by equivalent

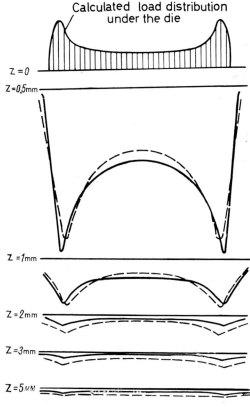

FIG. 51. Pressure distribution and vertical strains at various depths z when a cylindrical die is pressed into an elastic half-space

—— theoretical; - - - - experimental

concentrated forces, for which the corresponding stresses σ_z, σ_θ and σ_r at several points in each section are determined by the principle of superposition.

The calculation was made with the well known formulae [37] for the effect of a concentrated force acting on an elastic half-space (Boussinesq's problem):

$$\sigma_r = \frac{P}{2\pi} \left\{ (1 - 2\mu) \left[\frac{1}{r^2} - \frac{z}{r^2} (r^2 + z^2)^{-1/2} \right] - 3r^2z (r^2 + z^2)^{-5/2} \right\},$$

$$\sigma_\theta = \frac{P}{2\pi} (1 - 2\mu) \left[-\frac{1}{r^2} + \frac{z}{r^2} (r^2 + z^2)^{-1/2} + z (r^2 + z^2)^{-3/2} \right],$$

$$\sigma_z = \frac{3P}{2\pi} z^3 (r^2 + z^2)^{-5/2}$$

where μ is Poisson's ratio;

P is the equivalent concentrated compressive force;

z is the depth of the point examined below the surface where P is applied;

r is its distance from the z-axis (see Fig. 50).

The magnitudes of the strains ε_z, ε_x and ε_y at the same points were obtained from the stresses by the formulae given on page 95.

As a qualitative comparison of the data obtained experimentally and theoretically, Fig. 51 shows the distribution of the vertical strains at various depths. The curves show good agreement between the experimental and theoretical solutions for the distribution of the vertical strains under the given die dimensions.

Pressure of a concentrated force on an elastic half-space

In this example the specimen was loaded by a cone-shaped die acting as a concentrated force. The specimen, taken as an elastic half-space in the calculations, was a circular cylinder 150 mm in diameter and 160 mm high.

The test was carried out on a universal press type UP–6. The working pressure reached 250 kg/cm² (3500 lb/in²).

Wire strain gauges were placed at nine points along the vertical z-axis (Fig. 52). Unbonded gauges with a gauge length of 2 mm were used. Measurements were taken at five loads between 50 and 250 kg (the load was applied in stages of 50 kg each). The

curves for the experimental stress values under the loads used
in the test are given in Fig. 52.

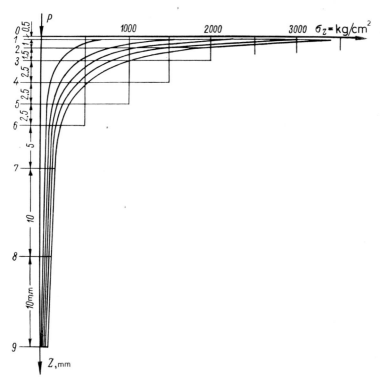

FIG. 52. Experimental curves for the stresses σ_z when a concentrated force is acting on an elastic half-space
1—9 denote the positions of the strain gauges

When a concentrated force is applied, the theoretical values of
the stresses in the elastic half-space (Fig. 50) at points in the line
of action of the force (z-axis) are determined by the formula

$$\sigma_z = \frac{3\,P}{2\pi\,z^2}\,.$$

A comparison between the stresses obtained by theoretical
calculations with this formula and those obtained experimentally

shows satisfactory agreement. To a depth of 2–3 mm the difference does not exceed 5%; in deeper layers it increases slightly and reaches 15–20%.

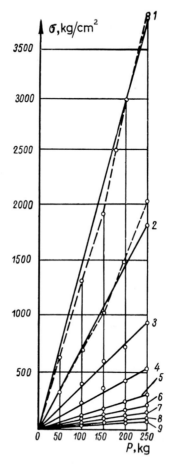

FIG. 53. Curves of $\sigma_z = f(P)$
at points 1–9

One of the reasons for this difference is the fact that the theoretical and experimental conditions do not completely coincide; for it is impossible to transmit a concentrated load in practice. In

the test described the point of the tapered die had the form of
a circular surface of about 0.10 cm² area.

In view of this presence of a surface of contact, the stresses
σ_z were also computed for the case of a load uniformly distributed over a circle of $A = 0.10$ cm² area by the formula

$$\sigma_z = \frac{P}{A}\left[-1 + \frac{z^3}{(a^2 + z^2)^{3/2}}\right],$$

where a is the radius of the circle of contact.

The theoretical calculations for the stresses σ_z then show that
near the region of contact the measured stresses are greater than
the calculated stresses, while at a certain depth the calculated
stresses are greater than the measured stresses.

The reverse is true for the calculations assuming a concentrated
force, where near the region of contact the measured stresses are
smaller than those obtained by calculation, while at a certain
depth in the elastic half-space the measured stresses are greater
than the calculated stresses.

This proves that the actual method of load transmission must
have been intermediate between the assumptions for these two
systems of calculation.

It can be seen from the curves given in Fig. 52 that the character of the stress distribution agrees well with data obtained
theoretically or by other experimental methods, for example
photoelasticity [37, 4].

The agreement between the experimental and calculated data
is also confirmed by the linear relationship between the stresses
and the loads (Fig. 53), which is precisely as expected from the
calculations for a concentrated force. In Fig. 53 the broken lines
have been plotted from experimental data, while the continuous
lines represent linear interpolations.

Pressure of a rigid sphere on an elastic half-space

A cylindrical specimen was again used and the strain gauges
with a gauge length of 2 mm were placed into one point on the
vertical axis passing through the centre of the surface of contact.

A particular feature of this and similar experiments is that the strain gauges can be positioned to allow for peculiarities in the shape of the testpiece.

The magnitudes of the strains at different depths from the boundary of the elastic half-space (the surface of the specimen) can be determined either by installing unbonded strain gauges at

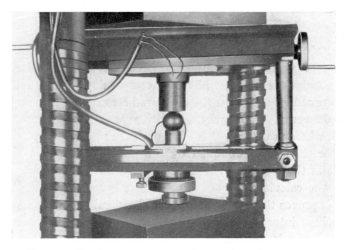

FIG. 54. Testing arrangement for a sphere pressing on an elastic half-space

different depths or by installing strain gauges at a single point only and successively moving this point nearer to the surface.

The second technique was used in this instance. The strain gauges located at a single point were gradually brought closer to the surface of the specimen (surface of contact) by successively removing layers of the specimen by machining.

The gauges were initially at a depth of 23.5 mm; for the final loading they were at a distance of 1.0 mm from the surface (Section 1–1 in Fig. 56) and, allowing for the active gauge length of 2 mm, measured the stresses at an average depth of 1.5–2 mm.

The specimen was loaded by means of a steel sphere. The surface of contact (point of application of the force) was moved along a diameter of the upper face of the cylinder. Measurements were taken at five points along this axis, namely where the gauges were located ($x = 0$) and at distances of 5 and 10 mm on either side.

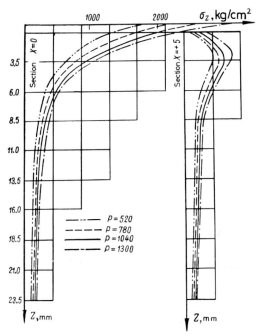

FIG. 55. Experimental curves for the stresses σ_z under a sphere pressing on an elastic half-space

The tests were carried out on a hydraulic press of six tons capacity (Fig. 54). At each point the load was applied in stages of 520, 680, 1040 and 1300 kg. The static strain measuring equipment was used.

The experimental data obtained are shown in Fig. 55 in the form of curves for the vertical stresses σ_z when the point of loading is directly above the strain gauges ($x = 0$) and when it is 5 mm ($x = 5$) from the vertical axis passing through the position of the gauges.

If the elastic characteristics of specimen and die are taken into account (the elastic moduli of the materials are 3.5×10^4 and 2.1×10^6 kg/cm²), this problem can be solved theoretically on the

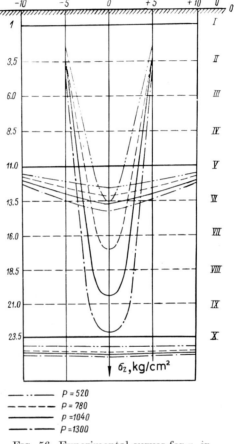

FIG. 56. Experimental curves for σ_z in Sections I, V and X

assumption of an absolutely rigid sphere (die) pressing on an elastic half-space. The calculated stresses for this system lead, for example, to a maximum stress $\sigma_z = 2710$ kg/cm² for a load $P = 1040$ kg located at $x = 0$. Extrapolation of the experimental stress curves (Fig. 55, Section $x = 0$) gives values close to the calculated stresses and thus indicates satisfactory agreement between experimental and calculated results.

Figure 56 gives examples of curves plotted from experimental data under four loads and shows the stress distribution in Sections I, V and X located at depths of 1.0, 11.0 and 23.5 mm. The measurements were taken for five different points of loading (abscissae x equal to 0, $+5$, $+10$, -5 and -10 mm).

21. OTHER EXAMPLES FOR THE USE OF SHORT GAUGE-LENGTH UNBONDED STRAIN GAUGES

Two examples for the use of a system of unbonded strain gauges, namely the direct measurement of stresses in a metallic component and the study of strains in the elastic-plastic region are given in this section.

The measurement of stresses inside a metal specimen

The study of stresses in models has a number of advantages: models can be made to any scale in relation to the actual structure; the work is carried out under laboratory conditions; separate account can be taken of individual factors during the investigation, etc. However, the subsequent conversion to real structures of different dimensions and different elastic characteristics presents difficulties in some cases (see Section 16).

The results given here have been obtained from stress measurements with the aid of unbonded wire strain gauges placed directly inside a metal specimen.

Holes 1.5–2 mm in diameter were drilled in the metal specimen. Strain gauges with a gauge length of 1.75 mm were placed at various depths in these holes: gauge 1 (Fig. 57) was placed at a depth of 1 mm, gauge 2 at a depth of 2 mm and gauge 3 at a depth of 3 mm. The holes were then filled up with a composition made from epoxy resin which was allowed to cure; the surface of the specimen was then machined. As a result, the strain gauges finished up inside the metal specimen at various distances from the surface under load.

In the test described, the holes were drilled so as to be in the line of action of the load.

Generally speaking, holes in a metal specimen impair its continuity to a certain extent; the influence they exert on the state of stress requires further investigation. It is known, for instance, that a hole exerts a pronounced influence if it intersects the direction of the strains to be measured.

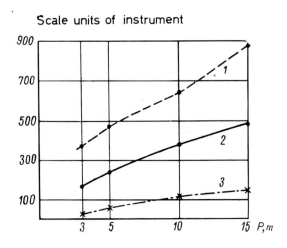

FIG. 57. Graphs of instrument readings for three unbonded wire strain gauges mounted in metal

In this test, however, where the holes are positioned vertically (coinciding with the orientation of the gauge) and the load is also acting in a vertical direction, the influence of the hole on the magnitude of the vertical strains is apparently quite insignificant.

First, the region of compressed material near the surface of contact can be assumed to represent a statically indeterminate system of metal and resin columns under compression. It is well known that in such a system the force distribution is proportional to the rigidity of the members so that obviously a column of resin with a cross-sectional area of 1.5–3 mm² can exert no substantial influence when the overall area of the surface of contact is about 300–400 mm².

The method is sometimes used in practice, for example in the study of stresses in reinforced concrete slabs; suitable openings, slots and holes are left and wire strain gauges or other strain measuring devices fixed to their walls. When strain measuring devices other than strain gauges are employed, the holes are left entirely unfilled. The authors propose to fill the holes with epoxy-resin-based material showing a good adhesion to the metal. The holes will therefore interfere with the homogeneity of the material but not with its continuity.

Secondly, if the strains are measured in the direction of the force, it should be borne in mind that for such a small ratio of the area of the resin-filled hole to that of the metallic cross-section, the strains in the direction of the force are determined by the metal and not by the resin core. Therefore, the strains along the resin core are the same as those in the metal. The strains in the other two directions depend on Poisson's ratio of the material and on the magnitude of the longitudinal strain in the direction of the force.

As regards the influence of the hole on the transverse strains, it should be remembered that Poisson's ratios of the resin and the metal have about the same value and that the strains across the resin core are determined by strains in the basic metal in which the core of epoxy-resin material is merely an inclusion.

Figure 57 shows the results of tests in which pressure is exerted on a cylindrical surface of 300 mm radius by a metal die of 500 mm radius. From the graphs it is evident that the gauges are quite sensitive to strain. The sensitivity of the static measuring instrument was 1×10^{-5} strain and readings were obtained up to 880 units, corresponding to about 4×10^{-3} strain (the stresses in steel are then about 8000 kg/cm² or 114,000 lb/in.²).

The tests were not intended to provide the solution to any specific problem; they merely served to show the possibility of installing strain gauges in metallic members. This idea requires further experimental and theoretical evidence about the influence of a local inhomogeneity due to the presence in a metal of a small hole filled with an epoxy-resin composition adhering well to the metal.

The measurement of strains in the elastic-plastic region

The second example in this section deals with an attempt to measure strains when the resin material is in its plastic range. i.e. in the range of permanent deformations.

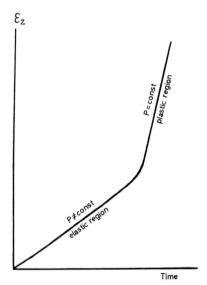

Fig. 58. Graph of instrument readings for strain gauges in the case of plastic deformations

None of the existing methods of measuring strains can be used to determine the strains occurring in the internal fibres of a material when the component is loaded to its plastic range. The grid method gives plastic deformations only on the surface of a component. The photoelastic method is used only in the elastic range of the model material. The X-ray diffraction method measures only residual stresses remaining after the loads have been removed.

The well known experiments on plastic strains [40] have been carried out with specimens entirely in a state of elastic-plastic deformation, mainly tubes or rods. If short gauge-length strain gauges are introduced, the elastic-plastic strains can also be studied in small individual regions inside the body of a member. With wire strain gauges, the distribution of the plastic strain intensities in the body of a model can be recorded as a function of time.

Figure 58 shows an oscillogram of the measured strain ε_z in a cylindrical specimen made from an epoxy-resin material. The specimen was compressed longitudinally until plastic strains appeared. It can be seen that the character of the curve is similar to the autographic strain record of a specimen tested on a Gagarin testing machine.

Consequently, a strain gauge placed inside a specimen can reflect the strains in the plastic range as well as in the elastic range.

CHAPTER IV

EXAMPLES FOR THE EXPERIMENTAL STUDY OF INTERNAL STRESSES UNDER DYNAMIC CONDITIONS

EXPERIMENTAL work involves the measurement of stresses in widely differing engineering structures and machine components. Although in structures one most frequently encounters static operating conditions, in machines and mechanisms the operation of the components is usually dynamic (parts of lathes, engines, means of transport, etc.). In some cases the loads are applied by impact (parts of forging presses, crankshafts and connecting-rods, etc.).

The existing methods for the calculation of dynamically loaded structures are based on static conditions. The dynamic character of the loads in one form or another is allowed for either in the assumed magnitude of the acting force or in the magnitude of the permissible stresses.

It is well known that a static system cannot simulate all the circumstances deforming a component under dynamic loads (for example the oscillations of a beam on continuous elastic foundations under a moving load). Therefore, the calculated results are usually approximate. In certain cases, for instance impacted components, the calculations become very involved.

For dynamic stress analysis experimental investigations are of paramount importance. In these cases the suggested method of measuring stresses with the aid of unbonded wire strain gauges is practically the only method of studying the stresses inside a component.

The engineering industry is constantly meeting new problems concerning the determination of contact strength of structural and machine components under dynamic loading, but the cur-

rent state of theoretical knowledge is not sufficiently advanced
to solve these problems without resort to special experimental
investigations.

As has been stated by Shtayerman [39], the efforts of engineers
and technicians in the last 60 years have been mainly directed
towards experimental verification of theory and its increasing
application to engineering problems. We give here a few examples
for experimental stress analysis of plane and three-dimensional
states of stresses under dynamic loads.

22. THE MEASUREMENT OF FIBRE STRESSES AND OTHER PRINCIPAL STRESSES IN A BEAM

Let us examine the results of measuring certain principal
stresses and fibre stresses in a beam on two supports loaded by a
force in the centre.

The model is 240 mm long, 25 mm wide and 34 mm high (Fig.
59). The strain gauges 1 and 2 are orientated at 45° to the longi-

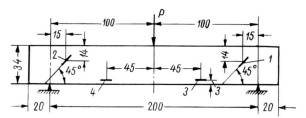

FIG. 59. Positions of wire strain gauges in a beam

tudinal edges of the beam, i.e. approximately in the direction of
the principal stresses at the points 1 and 2. It is well known that
oblique reinforcements have to be placed in these positions for
example in reinforced concrete beams under similar loading conditions. Theory shows that for the chosen orientations of these
two strain gauges the indicated principal stresses are of opposite
sign.

Two other strain gauges, 3 and 4, are located in the lower,
tensioned fibres of the beam. With the given loading arrangement the stresses at the points 3 and 4 should be equal.

8*

For testing purposes the beam was mounted in a special loading device (Fig. 60) in which the load was applied by a crank
lever made from sheet steel. A cyclically alternating load was
transmitted to one end of the lever by an eccentric mounted in
the chuck of a lathe. The bending force exerted on the test piece

FIG. 60. Loading device for dynamic tests on a beam

was controlled by the eccentricity of a cam acting on a spring.
The tests were conducted with three loading frequencies.

After the beam had been mounted in the loading device a small
initial load (10–15 kg) was applied. The maximum pressure on
the beam during the tests reached 50 kg/cm^2 (710 lb/in.^{2}).

The character of the strain-gauge signals can be seen from a
copy of the oscillograms (Fig. 61), recorded on an MPO–2 mirror oscillograph.

Gauges 1, 3 and 4 are located in the regions of tensile stress
and gauge 2 in a region of compressive stress. The sign of the
stresses is confirmed by the record.

Strain gauges 1 and 2 are orientated approximately in the direction of the principal stresses (the actual angle of the principal tensile stresses at the point of gauge 1 is 39°), therefore the sign of the strain will be the same as that of the corresponding

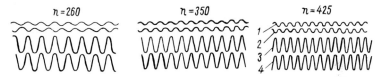

FIG. 61. Oscillograms of longitudinal and other principal stresses in a beam

principal stress. The oscillogram confirms the relationship of the calculated stresses and their signs (gauges 1, 3 and 4 have one sign of stress: tensile; gauge 2 has the opposite sign: compressive).

The design stresses at the points of the gauges were: gauge 1: 3.50, gauge 2: 3.0, gauges 3 and 4: 23 kg/cm^2 (50, 43 and 330 lb/in.^{2}).

Similar problems—the measurement of direct stresses with different orientations inside a component—are encountered quite frequently in design and research practice since beams and rods are the most frequently used shapes for the components of both machine elements and engineering structures.

Of course, the stresses in a rectangular beam of constant cross-section can be determined quite easily by calculation. However, in the design of machines and mechanisms various kinds of components are encountered more frequently than rectangular beams, for example components working as beams or rods under a complex combination of loads, components having complex cross-sections and varying lengths. In these cases the design stresses can only be determined approximately by means of laborious and complicated calculations; in some cases they can only be found by experiment.

23. THE MEASUREMENT OF STRESS CONCENTRATIONS

Stress concentrations under dynamic loading were measured in a plate with a central circular hole. The dimensions of the plate, the arrangement of the strain gauges and other data are given in Chapter III, Section 19.

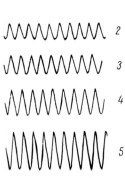

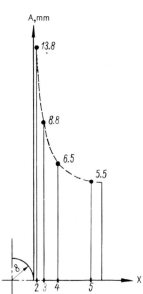

Fig. 62. Oscillograms of the stresses σ_y in a plate with a central circular hole

Fig. 63. Dynamic stress distribution σ_y in a plate with a central circular hole

The plate was mounted in a special device in which it was subjected to cyclic tensile loads. The loading frequency was about 100 c/min. The strains were recorded on an MPO–2 mirror oscillograph.

Figure 62 gives copies of the oscillograms for the stresses σ_y indicated by unbonded strain gauges on the horizontal axis of the central hole. The oscillograms are recorded signals of gauges 2, 3, 4 and 5 (Fig. 40).

The stress distribution obtained from the amplitudes of the records is given in Fig. 63; the figures indicate the amplitudes measured on the oscillograms.

To reduce static and dynamic results to a single scale, the curve is plotted with amplitudes magnified 6.5 times; the theoretical and experimental curves of the static tests can thus be compared with the data obtained from the dynamic tests. Comparison of the results of static and dynamic measurements (in relative ordinates from the curves, as also in absolute values of the dynamic stresses deduced from the recorded amplitudes after static calibration) shows that the stress distribution remains the same for dynamic as for static strains.

A dynamic process cannot always, however, be simulated by static tests as regards the magnitude of the force acting on a component. The study of stress concentrations under dynamic loads is an extremely important problem of experimental practice, particularly for real structures.

The experiment described is merely an example for possible applications of unbonded resistance wire strain gauges.

24. THE MEASUREMENT OF CONTACT STRESSES

The third example gives some of the results of measuring contact stresses under dynamic conditions. The investigation into contact stresses was conducted on a cylindrical specimen with a steel sphere pressing onto its upper surface. This case can be represented schematically as a sphere pressing on the plane boundary of an elastic half-space.

The tests were carried out on the loading device already used for measuring the stresses in a beam. A general view of the device with the testpiece for contact stresses is given in Fig. 64.

A strain gauge was placed in the test cylinder at a depth of 17.5 mm from the upper horizontal surface. After each test the strain gauge was brought closer to the upper surface of the specimen (the plane of application of the load) by machining away a layer of the model. For each level of the gauges the strains were determined and recorded on an oscillogram. The thickness

Fig. 64. Loading device for sphere exerting fluctuating pressure
on the plane surface of a circular cylindrical model

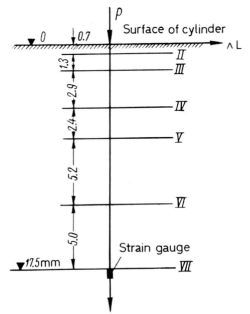

Fig. 65. Position of wire strain gauge
in the cylinder

of the layers removed from the model, as well as the depth of the gauge below the upper surface, are given in Fig. 65. Altogether five layers were machined away. In the final loading arrangement the gauge was at a depth of 0.7 mm from the surface of the cylinder. The oscillograms showing the strains at various depths of the cylinder under dynamic loading are given in Fig. 66 for

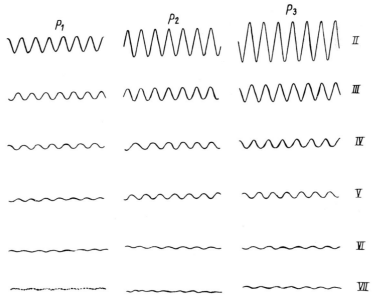

Fig. 66. Oscillograms of vertical strains at various depths under three fluctuating loads

the gauge positions in the layers I–VII numbered from the upper surface downwards.

The component was tested with three values of the vertical load. In these tests, as in the first example, an initial static pressure of 10–20 kg was superimposed on the working pressure applied by rotation of the eccentric. The testpiece thus carried an asymmetric load cycle. The magnitudes of the dynamic forces $P_1 = 20$, $P_2 = 50$ and $P_3 = 100$ kg were determined by static calibration from the strain indicated by the active strain gauge. Each column of the oscillograms in Fig. 66 corresponds to one of the loads.

A comparison of the experimental stresses with the stresses σ_z calculated on the assumption of a sphere pressing on an elastic half-space shows that the results are in satisfactory agreement.

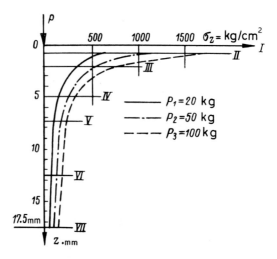

FIG. 67. Experimental curves for the stresses σ_z under fluctuating loads

The following data were used in the computation: sphere dia. 20 mm; for steel $E = 2.1 \times 10^6$ kg/mm² (30×10^6 lb/in²) and $\mu_1 = 0.33$; for the model material $E = 3.5 \times 10^4$ kg/cm² (0.5×10^6 lb/in²) and $\mu_2 = 0.36$. The calculation was carried out as described in Section 20. The variation of the contact stresses with depth is shown in Fig. 67.

Comparison of the experimental and theoretical results shows good agreement. The difference was within 5–10% for the loads P_2 and P_3; for P_1 the difference in the stresses was somewhat higher, which obviously can be explained by the insufficient sensitivity of the measuring equipment for such small strains.

The stresses in the surface of contact can be obtained by extrapolation of the experimental curves. It should be noted

that this extrapolation need only be carried out over an extremely limited region (between 0.5 and 1 mm) near the surface,
since for any orientation of the gauge the character of the stress
curve can be determined experimentally from this region down
to any depth.

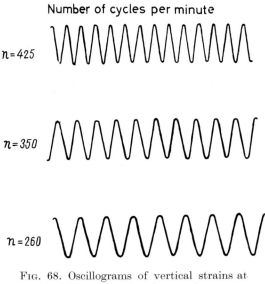

Number of cycles per minute

$n=425$

$n=350$

$n=260$

FIG. 68. Oscillograms of vertical strains at
different loading frequencies

It should also be noted that in the vast majority of cases the
stresses in the surface of contact can be obtained with comparative ease by calculation.

From the practical point of view, it is in the internal layers of
the contacting bodies and not at their surface, that investigation
of the contact stresses is required in many cases; for it is in
these internal layers that deep fractures (pitting) of the material
are caused by the high values of the principal shearing stresses.
For example rails, on which a considerable part of the metal
produced in Russia is spent, often have to be taken out of
service because of permanent strains and fractures caused
by deep failures in the stressed region under the surfaces of

contact. A similar pattern of failure is also observed in other cases of machine operation (pitting of rolls, rollers, gear wheels, etc.).

In the tests described measurements were taken at three loading frequencies. The number of cycles of load application as determined by the speed of the shaft with the eccentric was 425, 350 and 260 r.p.m. An analysis of the strain records at different frequencies (Fig. 68) indicates that in these tests the magnitude of the stresses depends to a certain extent upon the loading frequency. This, however, requires further confirmation and clarification of the quantitative relationships. Figure 68 gives portions of the oscillograms for the strain ε_z under the three loading frequencies.

The examples for dynamic stress measurement discussed here show that the method described can be widely used in scientific research and experimental work on the solution of various practical problems.

Of all the existing methods of stress analysis, only the photoelastic method is suitable for similar measurements. However, it can be used only for the investigation of plane states of stress. In addition, photoelastic measurements of this type require extremely laborious work in the evaluation of fringe patterns photographed at various instants of the dynamic strain cycle.

25. MEASUREMENT OF IMPACT STRESSES

The example given here describes an attempt to measure the stresses inside a model under the action of impact on its surface. The study of impact processes presents a difficult problem and one that occurs frequently in practice. The available theoretical solutions are so complicated that it is practically impossible to use them in engineering calculations.

In studies of the phenomena of collision between bodies, two parts of the state of stress have to be examined: the overall stresses occurring in the colliding bodies, and the localized stresses which occur near the points of contact. Although the first can be determined both theoretically and experimentally to some degree, it is quite impossible in the present state of knowledge to determine the second in a practical manner.

Its method of calculation is even more difficult and approximate (inaccurate) since the localized stresses frequently exceed the elastic limit and become residual. This happens because the impact time is very small (thousandths of a second), and the strain is unable to spread over the whole volume of the colliding

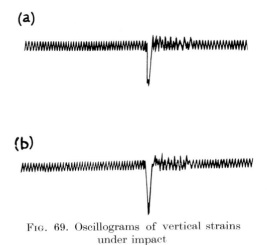

(a)

(b)

Fig. 69. Oscillograms of vertical strains
under impact

bodies. Moreover, in theoretical calculations it is difficult to allow for the influence exerted by the various types of inelastic strains of the system subjected to the impact (inelastic strains of the foundations).

For an investigation of impact phenomena it is also necessary to have special electric measuring equipment capable of recording high-frequency strains. In the authors' test the impact load was formed by a metallic sphere falling onto the surface of a cylinder. A short gauge-length unbonded wire strain gauge was placed in the cylindrical specimen at a depth of 0.5 mm from the impacted surface. The recording was made on a PMO–2 mirror oscillograph with a galvanometer element of type III with a natural frequency of 2 kc/s.

Figure 69 gives the vertical strain in the model near the point of impact of the sphere. The height of fall of the sphere in the second record [Fig. 69 (b)] is double that of the first [Fig. 69 (a)]. As can be seen from the record, if the height of fall of the sphere is doubled, the strain increases approximately 1.3 times.

The time of impact, judging by the time marks of the circuit vibrator which has a natural oscillation frequency of 500 c/s, is about 0.005–0.007 sec.

This experiment shows that in principle it is possible to apply the method of strain measurement with unbonded wire strain gauges to the study of highly dynamic processes and even to shock phenomena. Such phenomena are often encountered in modern high-speed engines, machines, machine tools, means of transport, forging and pressing equipment, etc.

CONCLUSION

ONE OF the main problems in the design and improvement of machines and mechanisms is the control of the strength of members and components.

A number of well known methods and techniques are employed for this purpose. The most widely used method, particularly for the study of dynamic processes, is one of the methods for the electrical measurement of non-electric quantities—namely the electrical method of strain measurement.

Of the various kinds of electric devices for strain measurement, resistance-wire strain gauges are used most frequently. They are small, of simple design, and can be mounted easily on components made from various materials. Their low inertia enables them to be used for highly dynamic (and even impact) phenomena.

Among the various kinds of practical problems, one frequently to be investigated is the state of stress at internal points in a variety of components under static and particularly dynamic loads.

The well known laws of the theory of elasticity relating strains to stresses show that for an investigation of the state of stress inside members all the three principal strains have to be measured, and that six strain components must be determined in the general case of arbitrary loads and an arbitrary position of the investigated point relative to the line of action of the resultant force. It is therefore impossible to determine the state of stress at internal points from the results of strain measurements in the surface layers of the component.

Such problems can be solved, however, by means of the electrical method of strain measurement described in this book, namely, strain measurement at internal points in components, or models of components, with the aid of special unbonded wire strain gauges placed inside the component (or model). The design of the strain gauges and the technique of introducing them into models allow the unbonded grids of the wire gauges to be placed into the model without upsetting the continuity and homogeneity of the material.

The dimensions of the unbonded strain gauges are such that strains can be measured at individual points in the model. The gauges can therefore be used for the measurement of localized concentrated stresses and contact stresses.

Due to the general advantages of electrical measurement of strains, the method described is suitable for the investigation of dynamic and even highly dynamic phenomena as also of elastic-plastic strains with a large stress gradient in the region of measurement, i.e. in the internal regions of a stress concentration.

The following conclusions can be drawn from the investigations discussed in this book:

1. One of the main problems in the application of stress analysis to machine components and structural members is the measurement of local and other stresses inside members and components, especially under present conditions when speeds and specified loads are increased while weights are reduced. The stresses at internal points of components, for example in the region of contact stresses, frequently determine the service life and strength of the members.
2. In view of the limited theoretical developments in the determination of contact and other internal stresses, a considerable part of stress analysis still depends on experimental work.
3. For an investigation of the stresses at internal points the strains must be measured at these points. Strains measured at the surface of a component cannot be used to determine the internal stresses, since the influence of the lateral strains then remains unknown.
4. None of the methods of measuring stresses used at present, apart from the photoelastic method, permits determination of the stresses at internal points of a body. The comparatively

laborious work and the special equipment and materials required considerably limit the use of the photoelastic method.

5. The proposed method of electrical measurement of strains with the aid of unbonded wire strain gauges makes it possible to investigate the state of stress at internal points of a body. The design and dimensions of the strain gauges allow strains to be measured practically at individual points.

6. The advantages of the electrical method of strain measurement enable the proposed technique to be employed for the measurement of stresses in components working under static and dynamic loads (even impact loads) in linear, plane and three-dimensional states of stress.

7. In principle, the method using unbonded wire strain gauges can be applied to measurements in the elastic–plastic range of a material, as well as to direct measurements in metallic components and other materials.

8. The proposed experimental work merely requires the usual strain-measuring equipment, together with materials already produced industrially.

REFERENCES

1. N. I. BEZUKHOV, *The theory of elasticity and plasticity, (Teoriya uprugosti i plastichnosti)*, Gostekhizdat, (1953).
2. S. N. NIKIFOROV, *The theory of elasticity and plasticity, (Teoriya uprugosti i plastichnosti)*, State Construction and Architecture Publishing House, Moscow, (1955).
3. C. C. PERRY and H. R. LISSNER, *The strain gauge primer*. McGraw-Hill, New York, (1955).
4. M. M. FROCHT, *Photoelasticity*, vols. I and II, Wiley, New York, (1948).
5. M. M. SAVERIN, *Contact strength of materials, (Kontaktnaya prochnost' materiala)* Book 2, Mashgiz, (1946).
6. I. I. IVASHKOV, *Contact strength of runners, (Kontaktnaya prochnost' begunkov)*, Mashgiz, (1954).
7. N. M. BELYAYEV, The problem of localized stresses in connection with the resistance of rails to warping, *Sb LIIPS*, **99** (1929).
8. N. M. BELYAYEV, Computation of maximum stresses during compression of contacting bodies, *Sb LIIPS*, **102** (1929).
9. N. P. RAYEVSKII, Experimental methods of investigation into mechanical parameters of machines, (Metody eksperimental'nogo issledovaniya mekhanicheskikh parametrov mashin), *Doklady Akad. Nauk SSSR*, (1952).
10. S. P. GONCHAROV, V. V. KITSENKO, A. S. MARGULIS and L. G. CHERNYAVSKII, *Measurement of Stresses and Forces, (Izmereniye napryazhenii i usilii)*, Mashgiz, (1955).
11. N. I. PROGOROVSKII, A. A. VASIL'YEV, V. I. BORTKEVICH and M. L. DAICHUK, *Wire Strain Gauges (Provolochnyye tenzometry)* Sb. izmereniye napryazhenii i usilii v detalyakh mashin, Mashgiz, (1955).
12. *Encyclopaedic handbook of mechanical engineering. (Entsiklopedicheskii spravochnik Mashinostroyeniya)*, vol. 1, Book 2. vol. 3, Mashgiz, (1948).
13. A. POLONSKII, The use of piezoelectric instruments, *Radio*, No. 4 (1953).
14. E. G. COKER and L. N. G. FILON, *A Treatise on Photo-elasticity*, Cambridge University Press, (1931).
15. M. V. MAL'TSEV, *X-radiography of Metals, (Rentgenografiya Metallov)*. Metallurgizdat, (1952).
16. M. P. ZHELDAK and G. V. KURDYUMOV, Determination of Residual Stresses by X-ray Diffraction, *Zh. Tekh. Fiz.*, **7** (1937).
17. M. P. ZHELDAK, G. V. KURDYUMOV and A. PROTOPOPOV, Determination of residual stresses by X-ray diffraction, *Zavodskaya Laboratoriya*, No. 7 (1934).

18. M. P. ZHELDAK and G. V. KURDYUMOV, The influence of stresses perpendicular to the surface on the magnitude of strains determined by X-ray diffraction, *Zavodskaya Laboratoriya*, No. 6 (1936).

19. A. P. KOMAR, The use of X-rays for the study of elastic stresses in crystalline substances, *Zh. Tekh. Fiz.*, **2** (1932).

20. M. A. BABICHEV, *Methods of Determining Internal Stresses in Machine Components, (Metody opredeleniya vnutrennikh napryazhenii v detalyakh mashin)*, Academy of Sciences, U. S. S. R., Moscow, (1955).

21. N. N. DAVIDENKOV and V. M. YAKUTOVICH, Experiments on the measurement of residual stresses in tubes, *Zh. Tekh. Fiz.*, **I.**, No. 23 (1931).

22. N. R. GONCHAROV, *Determination of Stresses in Machine Components by Means of Strain Gauges and Lacquers, (Opredeleniye napryazhenii v detalyakh mashin posredstvom tenzometrov i lakov)*, Mashgiz, (1946).

23. L. A. YEGOROV, The investigation of stresses in automobile components by the brittle coatings method. *Avtomobil'naya prom.*, No. 5 (1948).

24. I. S. KOZLOVSKII, The use of brittle coatings to obtain the stress distribution in machine components, *Amerikanskaya tekhnika i promyshlennost'*, No. 1 (1946).

25. N. M. BELYAYEV, *Strength of Materials, (Soprotivleniye materialov)*, Gostekhizdat, Moscow, (1953).

26. K. V. SEMENOV and V. V. SPRIOV, Powerful wire resistance transducers, *Zavodskaya Laboratoriya*, No. 3 (1953).

27. A. M. TURICHIN and P. V. NOVITSKII, *Wire strain gauges and their technical application (Provolochnyye preobrazovateli i ikh tekhnicheskoye primeneniye)*, Gosenergoizdat, (1957).

28. A. M. TURICHIN, *Electrical measurement of non-electric quantities (Elektricheskiye izmereniya neelektricheskikh velichin)*, Gosenergoizdat, (1954).

29. Material from the Plenary session of the Central Committee of the Communist Party of the Soviet Union, May. 6th 1958, (Materialy Plenuma TsK KPSS ot 6 maya 1958).

30. I. I. MATVEYEV, N. N. NASTAI, YE. K. PERMINOVA and YE. M. MOSKVINA, *Epoxy resins and their use (Epoksidnyye smoly i ikh primeneniye)*, LDNTP, (1957).

31. G. EPSHTEIN, *Cementing of Metals (Skleivaniye metallov)* Oborongiz, Moscow—Leningrad,(1957).

32. N. I. PRIGOROVSKII, A. K. PREIS, M. S. AKUTIN and B. S. GRACHEVA, Models made from ED-6 epoxy resin in the photoelastic method of stress analysis. *Zavodskaya Laboratoriya*, No. 4 (1957).

33. V. L. KIRPICHEV, *J. Russ. Chem. Soc.*, **6** (1874).

34. P. F. PAPKOVICH, *Theory of elasticity (Teoriya uprugosti)* Oborongiz, Moscow—Leningrad, (1939).

35. V. M. PROSHKO, *Models for stress analysis by the optical method. Studies on the theory of structures (Issledovaniya po teorii sooruzhenii)*, Stroiizdat, (1949).

36. S. G. LEKHNITSKII, The conversion of stresses in a transparent model to stresses in the actual component. Experimental Methods of determining stresses and strains in the elastic and plastic regions. *Sb. LGU* (1935).

37. S. P. TIMOSHENKO, *Theory of elasticity*, McGraw-Hill, New York, (1934).

38. N. M. BELYAYEV, The use of the Hertz theory for the computation of localized stresses at the point of contact between wheel and rail, *Vestnik inzhenerov*, No. 12 (1917).

39. I. YA. SHTAYERMAN, *The contact problem in the theory of elasticity (Kontaktnaya zadacha teorii uprugosti)*, Gostekhizdat, (1949).

40. A. A. IL'YUSHIN, *Plasticity (Plastichnost')*, Gostekhizdat, Moscow — Leningrad, (1948).

41. N. G. TISENKO and YU. M. MARGOLIN, Heat treatment of constantan for high-temperature wire resistance strain gauges, *Vestnik mashinostroyeniya*, No. 2 (1953).

42. *Wire Strain Measurement (Provolochnaya tenzometriya)*, LDNTP, 1 and 2 (1958).

43. I. YE. BYUS, The use of wire-resistance transducers in tests on bridges. *Tekhnika zheleznykh dorog*, No. 9 (1950).

INDEX